NOTHING BUT
ATOMS
AND MOLECULES ?

Probing the limits of science

Rodney D. Holder

STARNINE

First published 1993
This edition 1999

Unless otherwise indicated, biblical quotations are from
the King James Version

ISBN 0 9524752 1 9

British Library Cataloguing on Publication Data
A catalogue record for this book is available from the British Library.

Published in England by
StarNine Design
PO Box 100, Shipston on Stour,
Warwickshire CV36 5ZZ.

Contents

Science without religion is lame; religion without science is blind.

Albert Einstein

To my wife

Acknowledgements

In writing this book I owe a great debt of gratitude to many people. Of the authors I have read in the course of preparing and writing the book, perhaps the Rev Dr John Polkinghorne, former President of Queens' College, Cambridge, deserves special mention. It will be clear to readers that I have found his writing both stimulating and influential.

I am most grateful to those who took the time and trouble to comment on the manuscript, in part or whole, at various stages of its development. The Rev Dr Richard Burridge, Dean of King's College, London, made some very helpful comments on an outline of the book which were influential both on the shape the book took and some of the topics covered. Professor R. J. (Sam) Berry, Professor of Genetics, University College, London, made some extremely helpful comments on a complete draft of the manuscript, as did Dr Keith Dorrington, University Lecturer in Physiology and Fellow of University College, Oxford, and Professor Vern Farewell, Professor of Medical Statistics, University College, London.

While I am of the firm opinion that a work always improves as a result of critical comment, no doubt many errors and weaknesses remain; for these, of course, I accept full responsibility.

I am grateful to the following for granting permission to cite from the works quoted: Eileen O'Casey on behalf of the Estate of Sean O'Casey for the extract from *Juno and the Paycock*; The Society of Authors on behalf of the Bernard Shaw Estate for the line from *Arms and the Man*; A. P. Watt Ltd. on behalf of The Earl of Oxford and Asquith for the limerick by Monsignor Ronald Knox; and John Murray (Publishers) Ltd. for the extract from *Christmas* by Sir John Betjeman from his *Collected Poems*.

I am grateful to Tony Collins of Monarch Publications for overseeing the first edition of the book, and to Gerald Beckwith of StarNine Design for this reprinting. I have taken this opportunity to make a few minor corrections, but otherwise the book has not changed from the first edition.

Last, but by no means least, I owe a tremendous debt of gratitude to my dear wife, Shirley, without whom the book could certainly never have been written. She exhibited no small measure of self-sacrifice in supporting me in innumerable ways throughout the enterprise. A true labour of love.

CHAPTER 1

The Challenge Posed by 'Nothing-Buttery'

... True is it Nature hides
Her treasures less and less.— Man now presides
In power, where once he trembled in his weakness;
Science advances with gigantic strides;
But are we aught enriched in love and meekness?

(William Wordsworth, 1838, *Miscellaneous Sonnets,* Pt III, XLI,
To the Planet Venus.)

In a small book called *The Clockwork Image*[1] published in 1974
Professor Donald MacKay claimed to have coined the term 'nothing-buttery' some twenty-five years previously. MacKay, now sadly
deceased, was Professor of Communication at the University of
Keele and was engaged in research on the functioning of the human brain. He was also in the forefront of writers on the relationship between science and religious faith, and was himself a man of
deep faith. 'Nothing-buttery' was a deliberately pejorative term
coined to describe a prevalent attitude among scientists — that
more properly known as 'reductionism'. This is the attitude which
says that, if we have an explanation for a phenomenon in scientific
terms, then that is the only valid explanation. Moreover, nothing-buttery is characterized by the idea that there is a hierarchy among
the sciences, each of which can be completely explained in terms of
the next below it in the tree. Thus, psychology can be explained in
terms of biology, biology in terms of chemistry and chemistry in
terms of physics. What this implies is that literally everything is explained in terms of atoms and molecules and the laws governing them.

Indeed, taking the argument to its extreme, everything is everything is explained in terms of the ultimate constituents of matter, quarks and gluons, and these are explained by the mathematical equations describing their behaviour.

That nothing-buttery poses a serious challenge to a religious perspective on life is almost self-evident. My belief is that it is this philosophical position adopted by many scientists, with the propaganda put out in its favour, rather than any specific scientific theories, which has been the major contributory factor to the widespread acceptance in society that science and religious belief are not only in conflict but that science has made religion completely superfluous.

There can be no doubt that such a view is widely held. Whenever one talks of religious belief, one of the major objections presented is that surely science has disproved the claims of the major religions and offers a complete and satisfying explanation of how we got here and what we are. Science, in the popular mind, is associated with facts, which are established by experimental proof, whereas religion is associated with the dark forces of superstition.

Science is symbolic of the modern age. All around us we see its successes. Whenever we turn on a light, the triumph of science through the discovery of electricity is before us. The fruits of scientific research in the form of technological progress are modern miracles. We can see instantaneously on our television screens events happening on the other side of the world. Man has travelled to the moon and sent satellites to the edge of the solar system. We are living in the computer age: science and technology have given us machines which can perform tasks many millions of times faster than humans, and indeed there is now the almost frightening prospect of 'machine intelligence'. Modern medicine has an armoury of drugs and surgical techniques which can cure diseases in a way undreamt of 100 years ago. The contribution of science to the relief of human suffering is without parallel, and doctors and scientists are treated with the awe once accorded only to the priest.

The case has been put well by Jawaharlal Nehru:

It is science alone that can solve the problems of hunger and poverty, of sanitation and illiteracy, of superstition and deadening custom and tradition, of vast resources running to waste, of a rich country inhabited by starving people ... Who indeed could afford to ignore science today? At every turn we have to seek its aid ... The future belongs to science and those who make friends with science.[2]

In contrast, religion is assumed to be antiquated, superstitious, a relic of our mediaeval past. The Bible is full of contradictions and has been disproved by science. Darwin's theory of evolution provides the answer to how we got here, not the fanciful stories of the book of Genesis. And Darwin, like Galileo before him, was opposed by the church. The church is increasingly seen as irrelevant, unsure of what it believes (itself thrown into confusion by the scientific rationalism of the age), wrapped up in its own internal disputes and failing to minister to man's basic needs. As for miracles, only primitive people in an unscientific age could possibly believe in them. In any case it is difficult to believe in a God when you look at the sufferings of the world, which as often as not have been caused by religious wars! No, the continuing decline in church membership (only about 10% of the population in England now attend church)[3] is consonant with the rise of scientific enlightenment and the retreat of the dark forces of superstition.

Illustrative of this perception are the findings of an opinion poll for the *Daily Telegraph*,[4] among which were the following:

(i) Belief in a personal God declined from 41% of the population in 1957 to 30% in 1989.

(ii) Belief that Jesus was the Son of God declined from 71% to 46% over the same period; conversely belief that Jesus was just a man increased from 9% to 30%.

(iii) Belief that the New Testament is wholly or mostly of divine authority declined from 68% to 47% between 1960 and 1989; for the Old Testament the decline was from 60% to 43%.

The view that the Bible is mostly stories and fables increased correspondingly.

(iv) In only 5 years from 1984 to 1989 belief in the Gospel miracles as historical facts declined from 25% to 15%.

I believe that we can see in these findings the grinding penetration of scientific rationalism into the collective psyche. And supremely it is reductionism which is the culprit: the idea that we are *nothing but atoms and molecules*, and that a scientific explanation is the only valid one. Supernatural explanations are in contradiction to scientific ones, and have been superseded by them. In any case the supernatural cannot be weighed and measured after the fashion of science, and so, since it is not amenable to scientific investigation, it cannot exist.

Regrettably, nothing-buttery is still a very prevalent attitude among scientists, long after Professor MacKay's critique. In particular, it is epitomized, in rather different forms, in the writings of two of the best known and most illustrious of recent popularizers of science, Dr Richard Dawkins and Professor Stephen Hawking.

Richard Dawkins is Reader in Zoology at Oxford University and is a specialist in evolutionary biology. He sees evolution as not only the explanation for how we got here, but, rather perversely as it seems to me, for why we are here. The idea that science provides a total explanation is to be found near the beginning of *The Blind Watchmaker*:

> We wanted to know why we, and all other complicated things exist. And we can now answer that question ...[5]

There is a rather muddled use of language here, for we can all agree on the means even if we disagree as to the purpose. Dawkins really means that there is no purpose to life, since this is what the so-called 'purpose' of propagating our genes amounts to. As Mary Midgley points out, the ancient human longing is not for an explanation in terms of cause and effect, such as Dawkins provides, but a teleological one: 'the word is "why", not "how".'[6]

The thesis of *The Selfish Gene* is 'that we, and all other animals, are machines created by our genes'.[7] Human and animal behaviour, including such traits as altruism, are explicable solely in terms of genes, and our sole 'purpose' (though I have criticized the use of this word) as human beings is as 'gene survival machines'. In due course in this book I shall criticize both the claim that we are merely machines (albeit powerful and complex computers as Dawkins claims), and that we are here entirely for the benefit of reproducing our genes.

A constant theme of Dawkins is that, because evolution can explain how we arose as complex beings from primordial simplicity, there is no need to invoke a designer. The idea of God is therefore redundant. Here is another quotation from The Blind Watchmaker:

> The basic idea of *The Blind Watchmaker* is that we don't need to postulate a designer in order to understand life, or anything else in the universe.[8]

For Dawkins, in contrast to science which is concerned solely with evidence, religion is merely superstition with no foundation of evidence. Moreover, science provides a complete explanation (at least in principle) of the universe, so there is no need to invoke God as a cause:

> Scientific belief is based upon publicly checkable evidence. Religious faith not only lacks evidence; its independence from evidence is its joy, shouted from the rooftops ... Sophisticated theologians no longer claim literal truth for their holy books on questions such as the origin of the world and why living things appear to be well designed. Religion is no longer a serious candidate in the field of explanation. It is completely superseded by science.[9]

In his 1992 Voltaire Lecture, delivered to the British Humanist Association, Dawkins explained the root cause of religious belief in terms of epidemiology — it is a 'virus of the mind' spreading just like a computer virus. A feature of the lecture was the uncritical lumping together of the extremes of the religious spectrum. Thus a young child was 'easy prey to Moonies, scientologists and nuns'; mind-parasites, which gang together like genes for mutual support, form systems like 'Roman Catholicism or Voodoo'; and on the odd occasions when people are converted, rather than inherit the disease, this is because they have been exposed to an 'infective agent — a John Wesley, a Jim Jones or a St Paul'. Of course this is a game anybody can play — perhaps Dawkins's own virulent (I use the word advisedly) anti-religious outpourings are symptomatic of some mind infection!

When he writes about religion, which is quite often, Dawkins displays a vehemence, even a bitterness, bordering on the hysterical. Following the announcement in March 1993 that novelist Mrs Susan Howatch was to endow a lectureship at Cambridge University in science and theology, Dawkins wrote to *The Independent*, which had published a leader supporting the idea. Having rehearsed some of the achievements of science, he wrote of theology in the following terms:

> What has "theology" ever said that is of the smallest use to anybody? ... The achievements of theologians don't do anything, don't affect anything, don't achieve anything, don't even mean anything. What makes you think that "theology" is a subject at all?[10]

Strong words indeed, belying the image of cool detachment which the layman tends to associate with the scientist.

Stephen Hawking is Lucasian Professor of Mathematics at Cambridge, and as such holds the chair once held by Sir Isaac Newton. Having done seminal work on the theory of black holes, he is now working at the forefront of modern cosmology where the quest is on for a theory to unite the two great twentieth century revolutionary theories of physics — Einstein's general theory of relativity and the quantum theory of Planck, Schrödinger, and Heisenberg. His popular book *A Brief History of Time*, describing as it does one of the most exciting areas of modern science, broke all records in the best seller charts. It is also noteworthy that Hawking is a remarkable man whose genius has been exhibited with great personal courage in the face of extreme disability caused by amyotrophic lateral sclerosis.

Like Dawkins, Hawking sees science as explaining everything:

> Our goal is nothing less than a complete description of the universe we live in.[11]

Implicit in this quest is the assumption that a unified theory of physics, which is commonly referred to as a Theory of Everything (TOE), will not only explain the origin and evolution of the universe but also of life and the existence of human observers to speculate on these matters. That is to say, the reduction of psychology, biology and chemistry to physics is implicitly assumed.

Hawking talks much of God but sees him only in the narrow deistic sense of a First Cause, who may be responsible for the laws of nature, and who may have 'lit the blue touch paper' as it were at the beginning of time, but afterwards discreetly retired from the scene:

> These laws may have originally been decreed by God, but it appears that he has since left the universe to evolve according to them and does not now intervene in it.[12]

That this is a very naïve view of, at any rate, Christian theology, I shall discuss later. Hawking goes on to conclude that, in a universe with 'no boundary conditions' which he can envisage, there is no rôle at all for God, not even to light the blue touch paper:

> On the other hand, the quantum theory of gravity has opened up a new possibility, in which there would be no boundary to space-time and so there would be no need to specify the behavior [sic] at the boundary. There would be no singularities at which the laws of science broke down and no edge of space-time at which one would have to appeal to God or some new law to set the boundary conditions for space-time. One could say: "The boundary condition of the universe is that it has no boundary." The universe would be completely self-contained and not affected by anything outside itself. It would neither be created nor destroyed. It would just BE.[13]

Hawking describes how he put forward these ideas at a meeting at the Vatican and was worried that he might suffer the same fate as

Galileo. Hawking's recollection that the Pope counselled against inquiry into the moment of the Big Bang itself, since that was the work of God, is actually refuted by the official account.[14] Be that as it may (and we shall look in some detail at exactly what happened to Galileo, in due course), here is what Hawking goes on to say:

> The idea that space and time may form a closed surface without boundary also has profound implications for the role of God in the affairs of the universe. With the success of scientific theories in describing events, most people have come to believe that God allows the universe to evolve according to a set of laws and does not intervene in the universe to break these laws. However, the laws do not tell us what the universe should have looked like when it started — it would still be up to God to wind up the clockwork and choose how to start it off. So long as the universe had a beginning, we could suppose it had a creator. But if the universe is really completely self-contained, having no boundary or edge, it would have neither beginning nor end: it would simply be. What place, then, for a creator?[15]

Dawkins and Hawking are only the latest in a line of science popularizers who take this kind of approach, believing that scientific explanations supplant theological ones. Dr Peter Atkins is a lecturer in physical chemistry at Oxford and describes the aim of his book *The Creation* as follows:

> My aim is to argue that the universe can come into existence without intervention, and that there is no need to invoke the idea of a Supreme Being in one of its numerous manifestations. I have to accept, though, that anyone who is in some sense religious is not likely to be swayed by arguments like mine. Nevertheless, I hope that they will at least admit that science is extraordinarily strong and, if we disregard (as I argue we should) the question of a 'purpose' for the world, that it appears to be on the edge of explaining everything.[16]

Like Dawkins, Atkins thinks that the human brain is merely a complex organization of molecules that has come about through evolution. He says of human decision making:

At the deepest level, decisions are adjustments of the dispositions of atoms in the molecules inside large numbers of cells in the brain.[17]

He concludes:

Free will is merely the ability to decide, and the ability to decide is nothing other than the organized interplay of shifts of atoms responding to freedom as chance first endows them with energy to explore, and then traps them in new arrangements as their energy leaps naturally and randomly away. Even free will is ultimately corruption.[18]

We see in this quotation the tell-tale reductionist catch phrases—note the use of 'merely' and 'nothing other than'.

Atkins too invokes ideas from quantum theory in discussing how the universe might arise spontaneously with no need for a First Cause:

We can even begin to discern how the universe could come from absolute nothing as time induced (by chance) its own existence.[19]

And he adds:

We have been back to the time before time, and have tracked the lazy creator to his lair (he is, of course, not there).[20]

Carl Sagan is another writer with a reductionist frame of mind. He starts his book Cosmos, based on the television series of that name, by saying:

The Cosmos is all that ever was or ever will be.[21]

In ranging over the findings of modern science and speculating on the existence of life elsewhere in the universe, Sagan continues to betray this reductionist attitude. For example, he too regards the human brain as nothing but a complex machine which has evolved in a particular way.

In the biological field, zoologist Desmond Morris, author of such popular books as *The Naked Ape*,[22] *The Human Zoo*[23] and *Manwatching*,[24] can be cited as yet another writer who takes a reductionist line. Morris treats man as a social biological species and gains insights into human behaviour, often in an entertaining manner, by comparing man with the animals. He is so zealous to validate the comparison that he even perpetrates elementary zoological blunders. Thus he says, in attempting to explain the survival of large human groupings, which he dubs 'super-tribes': 'Bearing in mind our monkey ancestry, the social organization of surviving monkey species can provide us with some revealing clues.'[25] But we don't have a monkey ancestry! —according to the theory of evolution men and monkeys have a common ancestor. (Actually this error of Morris's was pointed out in a book written some years ago by the present Archbishop of Canterbury, Dr George Carey.[26])

Morris sees religion as performing an essentially biological function in the evolutionary process. It aids survival by providing a cohesive force within the super-tribe and a divisive force between super-tribes. Of course the gods who produce these effects have no objective existence: only their function is important.[27,28]

One could go on citing authors who, in writing about science, espouse a reductionist view. Rodney Cotterill, in writing about the human brain, points to the existence of the soul as 'mankind's greatest delusion'.[29] He adopts the same kind of strong reductionist stance as Atkins, Dawkins *et al*.

It is not clear to what extent these writers have thought through their reductionist position. Leaving aside for a moment the question of whether the reductionist approach is scientifically valid, it has devastating consequences for our view of our own humanity. For if we are nothing but atoms and molecules organized in a particular way through the chance processes of evolution, then love, beauty, good and evil, free will, reason itself — indeed all that makes us human and raises us above the rest of the created order — lose their meaning. Morality ceases to possess any basis of objectivity. Why should I love my neighbour, or go out of my way to help him? Rather, why should I not get everything I can for myself, trampling on whomsoever gets in my way? After all, I am nothing but a 'gene survival machine', and my sole 'purpose' is to propagate my own genes. The best we can do can be to come to some kind of agreement in our mutual interest along utilitarian lines to live in peace, but if it suits us we shall be free to break any such agreement. Our behaviour could degenerate to that which we see in the animal world —after all, we are just animals anyway.

Thus we begin to see that if the scientific reductionists are right then not only is religion destroyed but much else besides. In particular morality is undermined. In the twentieth century, we do not need to be reminded of the evils of racism, but perhaps racism is rather natural as a way of perpetuating one's genes. And what can be the justification for punishment when morality itself is no more?

In fact, science itself raises profound moral questions, which, especially in its reductionist dressing, it is powerless to answer. Lewis Wolpert, Professor of Biology at University College, London, believes that scientists bear no responsibility for how their discoveries are used, provided they enunciate the consequences of their research. He rightly sees that science gives its practitioners no special moral insights or knowledge.[30] Yet, where are these moral insights to come from if we are told that we are simply genetically programmed machines?

To give but two examples of areas where ethical issues are raised by science, we could name human embryology and environmental pollution. Traditional Judaeo-Christian ethical teaching stems from the belief that man, uniquely in creation, is accorded infinite value as being made in the image of God. This has profound consequences for the way we treat the weakest in society, including the unborn. These consequences are diametrically opposed to such ideas as eugenics, based on a primitive understanding of genetics, whereby we shall dispose of the defective and seek to generate a perfect race. Richard Dawkins's Darwinism leads him in another, but equally dangerous direction, namely the refutation of what he calls 'speciesism' and equation of the value of a human foetus to that of a chimpanzee.[31] In this he typifies the sort of perverted and unbalanced morality to which our society is tending, having been loosed from its Christian moorings.

Regarding pollution, the Christian starts from the position that the natural world is God's good creation, and that he has placed us in it as his stewards. This is the surest foundation for motivating a balanced and responsible treatment of nature and the environment. We reject these Christian insights at our peril.

It is reductionist philosophy which has provoked some of the recent attacks on science. People are beginning to see the dehumanizing impact of much that is said in the name of science and to react against it. One such writer is Fay Weldon who blames science for the loss of religious belief and says that substituting the Big Bang would leave mankind 'diminished and wretched'.[32] Another writer is Bryan Appleyard who accuses science of a 'power-crazed fantasy' in claiming to provide an explanation for everything.[33] He too is concerned at the destruction of values by the reductionist approach, and the denial of other means to attaining truth, eg the religious.

I believe that Weldon and Appleyard are over-reacting, but nevertheless that scientists have only themselves to blame for these attacks. Ultimately, however, it is not science that is to blame but the reductionist philosophy which is embraced by so many, but by no means all, scientists.

In fact, there are many scientists who are practising, orthodox Christian believers. A notable example is the Rev Dr John Polkinghorne, formerly Professor of Mathematical Physics at Cambridge University, who after a very successful career researching in quantum theory resigned his chair to enter the Anglican priesthood. Polkinghorne has written a number of books himself on the relationship between science and Christianity. The Revd Dr Arthur Peacocke is a physical biochemist, also turned Anglican priest, who as Director of the Ian Ramsay Centre, St Cross College, Oxford, is professionally concerned with issues in science and religion. Another Christian scientist is Sir John Houghton, former Professor of Atmospheric Physics at Oxford and now Director General of the Meteorological Office. Others include Sir Robert Boyd, former Professor of Physics at University College, London, and Professor R. J. (Sam) Berry, Professor of Genetics at University College, London. All of these men reject the reductionist approach of Dawkins *et al*, and find in contrast that qualities like love and beauty are meaningful, and that we can still talk of design in the universe despite the fact that we have scientific explanations for many phenomena.

One could go on naming eminent scientists who are practising Christians. We shall in any case come back to some of them in drawing on their writings, later in this book. It will be particularly important to look at the fact that historically many of the greatest scientists were Christians, indeed that modern science arose in a Christian culture. And while this may show that there are many people who are and have been able to hold these two strands of their lives together, as any good scientist knows, appeal to authority is no substitute for evidence. The prime aim of this book is to present the reader with evidence with which to judge for himself whether the reductionist position is warranted, or, conversely, whether it is reasonable to hold Christian beliefs in a scientific age. We shall be asking, 'Is reductionism valid, either as a programme of research or a philosophical position? Are science and faith really in conflict? Is faith indeed irrational as Dawkins thinks? Or rather is there any prospect for a coming together of the two disciplines of science and theology in providing complementary explanations for natural phenomena? And can scientific methods be applied to religious belief to validate it or otherwise?'

At the centre of the argument will be the issue of 'nothing-buttery' or reductionism. It is not so much the science of Dawkins and Hawking that is at fault–indeed much of what they say is a presentation of widely accepted, standard theories — but the false 'scientism' of the philosophical speculation and 'hype' with which they accompany their scientific accounts.

I hope to show that reductionism is in fact a fundamental error, and that for two main reasons. The first is that it fails in its own terms. The programme to reduce all the higher level sciences to physics, and ultimately to mathematics, is doomed to failure. Love and reason do have a meaning which is irreducible to the behaviour of atoms and molecules. Moreover, to discover an explanation of phenomena in scientific terms is not to exhaust all that can be said about those phenomena — a complementary explanation in terms of the working of God may be rationally held. The question of design is not answered by saying that we know that all the complexity and intricacy of the world arose through evolution by natural selection.

Secondly, reductionism fails is because, to use a rather ugly modern expression, the 'goal posts' are shifting. Our understanding of the physics and mathematics to which the aim is to reduce the other sciences has undergone radical change in the twentieth century. The old Newtonian mechanistic and deterministic view of the universe is shattered for ever, yet it is still to the Newtonian paradigm that appeal is made in reductionist arguments. Mathematics too has suffered its greatest crisis in the present century. If mathematics is not complete, as is now known to be the case, how can science which depends on it derive a complete explanation of phenomena?

We begin our investigation of these matters by rehearsing the modern scientific account of the origin and evolution of the universe and our place in it. We then examine how this view arose and the evidence adduced for it by scientists — how does science go about its business and what is the status of scientific theories? We look at the historical perspective as mentioned above, particularly the cultural context in which modern science arose. At this stage we also look at the two great historical controversies between science and faith, those involving Galileo and Darwin, and how Biblical interpretation bears on matters of science. Then comes our more detailed analysis of the metaphysical position of 'nothing-buttery' and our refutation of it in its own terms. We go on to discuss the crisis in mathematics and the breakdown of classical physics — vital to our second argument, referred to above, for the demise of reductionism. The discussion of 'nothing-buttery' culminates in our consideration of the most important manifestation of it, that is in the way it affects our view of man himself. Is conscious thought really to be equated with neurophysiological events in the cerebral cortex? Is man a gene survival machine, or merely some sort of complex computer?

I hope by then to have persuaded the reader of the bankruptcy of the reductionist position and we begin to look at some of the recent reactions to it. These include the wholesale rejection of science, which as I mentioned above I regard as an over-reaction. They also include the attempt to justify Eastern mysticism from modern physics, and consideration of a holistic theory of the Earth as a living organism (the so-called Gaia hypothesis) and the implications of that.

This leads on to a consideration of the claims of theism, that there is a God and that he can act in the world. We reconsider the argument from design, not only in the light of evolutionary biology, but in the light of very recent developments in astrophysics – developments which bring us right back to the debates of Copernicus and Galileo of the centrality of man in the cosmos. Consideration of modern developments in physics, such as quantum theory and the theory of chaos, also leads to new insights about how God might interact with his world.

We then expose traditional Christianity to the kind of scientific criteria for validity that we might expect of scientific theories, using the appropriate tools of historical and literary criticism as well as of natural science. My contention is that Christianity will bear this and can be accepted as rational in the same way as scientific theories — as for science, so for faith there is no absolute proof but there is much corroboratory evidence. Thus, while the embracing of Christianity must always remain a step of faith, I endeavour to show that it is not faith 'in a vacuum', nor irrational faith, but faith grounded on solid evidence, and might be accepted in the same way as scientific theories are accepted.

The main area of dispute between scientists and theologians is not so much the detail of particular scientific theories but the presuppositions brought to the exposition of science. Both evolutionary biology, rightly understood, and modern physics give insights into the universe and man's position in it which offer a more promising hope of synergy between science and theology than earlier mechanistic scientific theories. Of course theology too has its presuppositions and these must be open to scrutiny. I believe that reductionism in science has a close parallel in fundamentalism in religion, and we should be critical of both tendencies. Equally, extreme scepticism in both spheres is unjustified. I hope that readers can begin to see authentic science and theology as providing complementary rather than conflicting descriptions of 'the way the world is', to use Polkinghorne's recurring expression. Since all knowledge is ultimately knowledge of God, I am convinced that each discipline has much to learn from the other.

Finally, I draw the threads of the book together in a conclusion which I hope readers will find is a satisfying synthesis of what we can learn from a study of science and Christian faith.

Inevitably, some of the discussion that follows will be of a technical nature. The non-specialist reader is urged to skim over the detail, and concentrate on getting the gist of the argument from such passages. I believe that the effort to understand the main thesis is well worth making and, dare I say it, possibly even life-changing!

Let us begin our journey, then, by considering what precisely the scientists are telling us of our origins and place in the cosmos.

CHAPTER 2

The Scientific View of the World

An' as it blowed an' blowed
I often looked up at the sky
an 'assed meself the question,
what is the stars, what is the stars?

(Sean O'Casey, *Juno and the Paycock.*)

In this chapter I present a summary of the modern scientific view of the world as presented to us in popular writings by authors such as Stephen Hawking and Richard Dawkins. Leaving more detailed discussion of the logical and philosophical status of this view to the next chapter, I précis the scientific understanding of how the universe began and how it has evolved to produce human beings. Towards the end of the chapter I begin to disentangle the philosophical presuppositions of the popularizers from their genuine science.

The origin of the universe

The White Rabbit put on his spectacles. 'Where shall I begin, please your Majesty?' he asked.
'Begin at the beginning', the King said gravely, 'and go on till you come to the end: then stop.'

(Lewis Carroll, *Alice's Adventures in Wonderland.*)

According to modern cosmology, the universe began some 15,000 million years ago in a gigantic explosion — the hot Big Bang. Let us spend a few moments trying to understand how we know this.

The basic unit of matter in cosmology is the cluster of galaxies. Our own Milky Way Galaxy containing some 100,000 million stars, of which the sun is a very ordinary example lying, undistinguished, some two-thirds of the way out from the centre, belongs to a small cluster of about 20 galaxies called the Local Group. There are some million million galaxies in the observable universe and cluster sizes range from the singleton to upwards of a thousand members.

When we observe these basic units of matter, the clusters of galaxies, in the universe today, we notice a very curious thing. All these units are rushing away from us, and, moreover, the further they are away the faster they are receding. In fact, and this is very interesting as I shall explain, their speed of recession is directly proportional to their distance away. That is, if one galaxy is twice as far away as a second, the speed at which it is rushing away will be twice as great; if three times as far, then three times the speed, and so on.

Let us delve a bit deeper into this. When we observe a distant galaxy we examine the spectrum of the light entering our telescopes. This spectrum is crossed by dark lines at certain frequencies due to absorption by the atoms of various chemical elements. When the frequencies at which the absorption takes place are compared with those of the laboratory it is noticed that the galactic spectra are all shifted to the red. This is the well-known Doppler effect: the same effect is observed on a railway bridge when the high pitched noise of an approaching train turns to a lower pitch as the train recedes. By measuring the change in frequency we can derive the speed of the galaxy.

To measure the distance of a galaxy is rather more difficult, but once one galaxy's distance is obtained the distances of others can be derived by comparing brightnesses. Fortunately, nearby galactic distances can be measured since we can make out individual stars and the stellar distance scale is well established. There is in fact a progression of objects which is used to derive these distance scales. Thus, the distance of nearby stars is measured by the method of 'parallax', ie trigonometrically using the earth's orbit round the sun as baseline. Then it is known that the intrinsic brightness of certain classes of pulsating stars (called 'Cepheids' after their prototype

Delta Cephei) can be deduced from the period of pulsation — so given the distance of a near one the distances of others can be established from their intrinsic brightnesses. Similarly with galaxies we can measure the distance of a nearby one by making out Cepheid stars; for those further away we might make out brighter objects such as arise when a star explodes as a supernova, until ultimately we have to rely on the brightness of a whole galaxy as the key to its distance, assuming that similar looking galaxies have similar brightnesses.

Does the fact that galaxies are all receding from the earth place us in a privileged position in the universe? No! The velocity-distance proportionality law implies that if we moved to any other galaxy in the universe we would observe the same recession and the same proportionality. Moreover, it is remarkable that this is the only law for which this would hold.

The fact that galaxies are all moving away from each other has the natural corollary that they were all much closer at an earlier epoch in the universe's history. It would seem to be the case that if we extrapolate back far enough we should arrive at a time when the galaxies all coalesced at a point. It is in fact easy to get an estimate of when that time was if we assume that the expansion has been uniform: it is simply the distance of any galaxy divided by its speed (the same for all galaxies by the proportionality law). In this way we can derive the age of the universe.[1]

Clearly there are conceptual problems in taking the above calculation to its logical conclusion right back to the moment of the Big Bang itself. Nevertheless these problems are not as insuperable as might be supposed. We can safely consider times as early as one hundredth of a second from the Big Bang, since from then matter will be in a state which can be described by the known laws of physics. Cosmologists talk about earlier epochs when matter is in ever more esoteric states and only come truly unstuck at 10^{-43} seconds from the Big Bang at which time a presently non-existent theory of quantum gravity is needed!

The evolution of the universe

"This world was once a fluid haze of light,
Till toward the centre set the starry tides,
And eddied into suns, that whirling cast
The planets: then the monster, then the man; ..."

(Alfred, Lord Tennyson, 1847, *The Princess: a Medley,* II,
102-105, referring to the nebular hypothesis of Laplace.)

The insight of the expanding universe, discovered by Edwin
Hubble in the United States in the 1920s, has led us to hypothesize
that the universe started in an unbelievably compact state. Let us
now turn the tables and trace the history of the universe forward
from this early, dense condition.

As the expansion progresses, at a period of a few hundred thousand years after the initial Big Bang explosion, we have a gas which,
under the influence of gravitation, begins to form clumps. These
clumps are the galaxies and the stars within them. They arise because small, random fluctuations in the expanding gas give rise to
regions of enhanced density which have sufficient self-gravity to
retard them.

We now know a great deal about the formation and evolution
of stars. We can even see the birth of stars in swirling clouds of gas
today through our telescopes. As a gas cloud collapses its temperature rises until at its centre the temperature is so high that nuclear
reactions are triggered. It is through these nuclear reactions inside stars that the chemical elements are built up from the initial hydrogen provided by the Big Bang. The most massive, blue
stars evolve the most rapidly. When their nuclear fuel is spent
they become unstable and explode as supernovae in spectacular
fashion. Perhaps the most famous supernova was that observed
by Chinese astronomers in the year 1054 AD in the constella-
tion of Taurus. The remnant of this gigantic explosion can be
seen today.

Successive generations of supernovae have spewed out the heavier elements which they have created into the surrounding interstellar medium. About 4,500 million years ago our sun with its solar system was formed from this enriched material (we are made from the embers of supernova explosions!).[2] The sun is a very ordinary medium sized yellow star situated, as we have seen, inconspicuously, near the edge of the Milky Way Galaxy. It is some 860,000 miles across and is sustained in being, like all other stars, by the energy arising from nuclear reactions in its core. Mass is converted into energy through nuclear reactions in the sun's core at the rate of 4,000,000 tons per second. This is how the sun radiates and illuminates the earth and how it will continue to do so for several thousand million years to come!

The earth is a small planet orbiting the sun. Its chemical composition differs from that of the sun in being deficient in the light, volatile elements. However, when account is taken of the escape of these elements during planetary formation, it would appear that the sun and planets were formed from the same material. Also, independent confirmation of the age of the earth comes from measurements of the abundances of isotopes of certain elements in terrestrial rocks (radioactive dating).

The origin and evolution of life

This preservation of favourable individual differences and variation, and the destruction of those which are injurious, I have called Natural Selection, or the Survival of the Fittest

(Charles Darwin, *The Origin of Species*, 1859.[3])

At this point the chemists and biologists take up the story. The astrophysicists have given them the earth and a very long timespan in which to evolve human beings.

The atmosphere of the newly born earth would have consisted of a 'primordial soup' of simple chemicals, for example hydrogen, water, methane, ammonia and carbon monoxide. In this environment more complicated, organic molecules will be built up. Processes like this have been observed in the laboratory when such mixtures of chemicals have been subjected to electric discharges (which simulate lightning) and ultra violet radiation (which would have been more prevalent on earth before the formation of the ozone layer). Over a long period of time we see the formation of amino acids leading on to the formation of proteins, and of the purines and pyramidines, the building blocks of DNA and RNA, the large replicating molecules essential to life. It was probably a billion years after the earth came into existence that DNA was formed.

Once self-replicating life has developed, in however primitive a form, Darwinian evolution takes over. These living organisms evolve into higher species through the process of natural selection. Chance mutations which are conducive to survival in a competitive world survive, whereas those which are not die out. Survival for DNA, or more particularly the individual genes of which it is composed, is enhanced by the formation of protective cells to cocoon it, then by multi-cellular bodies, through to the explosive variety of animal life we witness in the fossil record and in nature today. Interestingly it is the earliest organisms, the blue-green algae, which transformed the atmosphere, releasing oxygen by the process of photosynthesis: we developed from them and without the oxygen they made we could not exist.

As Darwin came to realize, the key to speciation (formation of new species) is the geographical separation of members of a single species which then evolve and adapt to their different environments. It was John Gould of the London Zoo who demonstrated to Darwin that his bird specimens from the Galapagos Islands not only represented species distinct from those of the South American mainland, but also differed from island to island.[4]

One of the most significant developments of the evolutionary process was the emergence of sexual reproduction, though the details of how this arose remain a puzzle.[5] It confers enhanced survival advantage by providing much greater variation on which selection can work than asexual reproduction. It is particularly of value in a rapidly changing environment, where the identical progeny of parthenogenetically (ie asexually) reproducing species are at a severe disadvantage.

In the end, about 2 to 4 million years ago, the natural selection of genetic mutations leads to human beings, who evolve from *Australopithecus* and *Homo erectus* through various stages to *Homo sapiens*. With conscious minds these are able to speculate on the meaning if any of their origins!

Natural selection is an hypothesis of extraordinary simplicity and explanatory power. The keys are: a very long period of time for complexity to evolve; the existence of chance mutations (now known to be copying errors in the genetic code and whose rate of occurrence is enhanced by chemical and radioactive means); the step by step selection of the (comparatively very rare) mutations which enhance survival prospects in a nature 'red in tooth and claw'; and geographical separation of members of a species by natural barriers (eg rivers and mountains). Given 3½ billion years, as Dawkins shows, the selection of mutations favourable to survival gives rise to systems as diverse and complex as bat sonar and the human eye.[6]

Of course neither Darwin nor Alfred Russell Wallace, who independently discovered the principle of natural selection, knew of the genetic basis of evolution. This only came about through the work of Gregor Mendel on inheritance and, of course, modern molecular biology, culminating in the discovery in 1953 in Cambridge by Crick and Watson of the famous double helix structure of the DNA molecule. Watson recounts how, at lunch-time on the day the jig-saw pieces were finally falling into place, his colleague 'winged into' their local Cambridge hostelry, the Eagle, and announced to all within earshot that they had found 'the secret of life'.[7]

Mendel, an Austrian monk of the Augustinian order, by crossing certain varieties of garden pea, observed that characteristics such as flower colour were inherited from one or other parent and not blended. Thus he postulated basic units or 'elements' of inheritance, and furthermore that these were of two types, dominant or recessive. If a plant inherited two dominant elements or one dominant and one recessive for a trait, the dominant trait would be observed. Only if two recessive elements for a trait were inherited would that trait be observed. The 'elements' which Mendel postulated are what we now know as genes.

The modern theory of evolution, which ascribes a genetic origin to the mutations sifted by natural selection, is consequently known as the neo-Darwinian synthesis.

Reductionist Assumptions

For science can only ascertain what is, but not what should be, and outside its domain value judgments of all kinds remain necessary.

(Albert Einstein.[8])

It will be noticed that God is not mentioned or even, seemingly, needed in the scenario I have described. In the words of Laplace when challenged by Napoleon on the rôle of God in his mechanistic scheme of the universe, 'Sire, I have no need of that hypothesis'. From the Big Bang onwards the whole process runs itself like clockwork according to the laws of nature. And as we saw in Chapter 1, it is increasingly looking as though God is not necessarily required even at the Big Bang itself, to light the blue touch paper and retire. Advances in physics are pushing back the frontier further and further.

It is here that I want to begin to take some of the science popularizers to task; I shall elaborate these criticisms later. The picture presented above is a scientific account. It provides an explanation as to how the universe has evolved and man has appeared on the scene. And one does not normally find God referred to in scientific papers or books.

It is Hawking and Dawkins who in their different ways overstep the boundaries of science by claiming that, because God does not occur in their science, he does not exist. They present the scientific account, but accompany it with all kinds of unjustified metaphysical statements. For example, because the scientific account of biological evolution does not mention purpose, Dawkins concludes that there is no purpose, or, alternatively, the purpose of human beings is merely to propagate their genes. But, as Stanley Jaki observes, 'His most purposeful campaign against purpose in nature offered one more startling bit of evidence about man's ability to know design and act purposively'.[9] Jaki goes on to say, referring especially to Jacques Monod's *Chance and Necessity*, but the same could be said of *The Blind Watchmaker* and *The Selfish Gene*, that 'every book is a tangible witness to purpose, to final cause, which is so different from the efficient cause as to never contradict any of the conservation laws of physics'.[10] Just so, the scientific account deals only with efficient causes in Aristotle's terminology: it has nothing to say of final causes.

For Dawkins, God has been eliminated from the creation of animals and humans because this is explained by natural selection. For Stephen Hawking God is eliminated because the singularity in space-time at the moment of the Big Bang can be 'smoothed out'. As we shall see in more detail later, this still leaves us with the question, 'Why is there anything at all? ' and it ignores God's ongoing activity. As Hawking himself puts it, perhaps not clear in his own mind that he has truly eliminated the need for a creator:

> What is it that breathes fire into the equations and makes a universe for them to describe? The usual approach of science of constructing a mathematical model cannot answer the questions of why there should be a universe for the model to describe. Why does the universe go to all the bother of existing? Is the unified theory so compelling that it brings about its own existence? Or does it need a creator, and, if so, does he have any other effect on the universe? And who created him?[11]

The bare scientific statement of the process whereby the universe and man have evolved does not answer the question why all this has happened. Admittedly it raises questions for a religious perspective, eg how do we square this account with primitive, religious cosmologies, and how do we ascribe meaning or see God at work when chance seems to play such a part in the whole process?

But such a part cannot be ruled out *a priori*, rather we must look to see if there is evidence elsewhere for such a view. The assumption that there is no purpose is just that — a metaphysical assumption which must be judged by the criteria appropriate to metaphysics, rather than natural science. As a metaphysical assumption it has no place in a scientific treatise.

Further, it is not necessary in order for the above account to be valid that we accept that all the sciences can be reduced to physics. Physics is predominant in cosmology, but in evolution we have introduced both chemistry and biology — natural selection is fundamentally a biological concept. And while the human brain may have evolved through chemical and biological processes, and animal behaviour may be governed by genetic programming, we do not have to believe that our minds and corresponding behaviour are purely mechanistic and that our values of goodness, beauty and so on are illusory. No, again these questions must all be judged by criteria outside the realm of science, which just tells us how complex structures arose from simple beginnings. Science can neither ascribe nor deny meaning to such concepts.

All this begs the question of the status and scope of scientific theories. As I have said, my main aim is not so much to challenge the scientific account *per se* but the philosophical baggage that so often accompanies it. Having done research in astrophysics myself, I accept the broad scientific picture of the origin and evolution of the universe presented earlier in this chapter. Since biologists apply the same kind of scientific method to their field of study, I am also confident in accepting the picture they give of evolution by natural selection. Yet it is important to recognise that there is no ultimate proof of any scientific theory, that other theories may come along and supplant the present ones, and that at any one time we only have an approximate picture of reality. These considerations are the subject of my next chapter.

CHAPTER 3

Where did this view come from ? – Scientific Method

Now, what I want is, Facts. Teach these boys and girls nothing but Facts. Facts alone are wanted in life. Plant nothing else, and root out everything else. You can only form the minds of reasoning animals upon Facts: nothing else will ever be of any service to them. This is the principle on which I bring up my own children, and this is the principle on which I bring up these children. Stick to Facts, Sir!

(Charles Dickens, *Hard Times,*Chapter 1.)

In the preceding chapter I presented a summary of the scientific view of the world with a confidence which many scientists would eschew. Let us now proceed to examine the nature of scientific laws and how scientists go about their business.

Scientific laws

Nature and Nature's laws lay hid in night:
God said, Let Newton be! and all was light.

(Alexander Pope.[1])

The view of the universe described in the preceding chapter has been developed using scientific laws, the so-called 'laws of nature'. Examples of basic scientific laws include, for example, Newton's famous laws of motion:

(i)   A body will continue in its state of rest or uniform motion in a straight line, unless acted on by a force.

(ii)   The force acting on a body gives rise to an acceleration of the body as described by the formula

force = mass x acceleration

(iii) To every action there is an equal and opposite reaction.

In addition to these ought to be mentioned Newton's law of gravitation, that the gravitational force between two bodies is proportional to the product of their masses and inversely proportional to the square of the distance between them. Assuming these laws we can predict the behaviour of matter, as described in the previous chapter (actually this statement needs to be qualified as we shall see later).

In the biological sphere the law of the survival of the fittest (natural selection) might also be regarded as a law of nature.

What is the status of these laws? Why should we believe them and how reliable are they?

Science attempts to look at the world objectively. It makes observations, analyses and classifies those observations, draws conclusions from them and makes predictions. When the predictions are verified, the scientist feels he is on the right lines. Science today is very much an international enterprise with many different laboratories round the world eager to repeat a reported experiment and verify a new theory. An interesting example in 1989 was the reporting by Fleischmann and Pons of the achievement of nuclear fusion at room temperature, of major importance for producing cheap energy if verified. On this occasion, however, other laboratories failed to repeat the experiment successfully, so cold nuclear fusion has not been accepted by the scientific community.[2,3] Another example was the reported change in mass of a spinning gyroscope, which would have violated Newton's law if verified. However, again repetition of the experiment by other scientists failed to corroborate these findings.

An important element of scientific method is the isolation, as far as possible, of the phenomenon under investigation, and the dismissal of extraneous effects. Thus in early investigations of dynamics, by Galileo and Newton, the effects of air resistance were neglected, since these were regarded as minor perturbations on the motion of solid bodies. In the real world such effects will of course always be present, so the laws derived will only ever approximately describe reality. It is an interesting and important question, therefore, as to whether we can ever uncover universal laws by our experimental procedures, or whether the laws themselves are approximate.

Having made the above remarks about the objectivity of science, and ignoring for the moment the question of approximation, it must now be said that the scientific method is by no means beyond criticism. Science proceeds by the 'principle of induction', which entails drawing general conclusions from particular instances. For example, by observing that some polar bears are white, the general conclusion that all polar bears are white is drawn. This is a logically dubious procedure. Hume indeed in the eighteenth century stated that universal propositions could not be verified by observations. Strictly speaking, in order to verify the proposition about polar bears, all polar bears in the universe should be observed, clearly an impossible task.

That the idea of verification is problematic might be illuminated if we consider that the statement 'All polar bears are white' is logically exactly equivalent to the statement 'All non-white objects are not polar bears'. In this way we can see that a brown chimpanzee may be adduced as evidence in favour of the proposition that all polar bears are white!

In the light of such problems, Sir Karl Popper introduced the contrary notion of falsifiability to the philosophy of science. An hypothesis cannot be verified but it can most certainly be falsified. A single instance of a black polar bear would falsify the statement 'All polar bears are white'.

In his book *The Emperor's New Mind* [4] Roger Penrose, Rouse Ball Professor of Mathematics at Oxford University, classifies scientific theories into the categories of 'superb', 'useful' or 'tentative' depending on their elegance, the degree to which they have stood the test of time, and their accuracy of prediction. But according to Popper all scientific theories are tentative. Essentially, scientific progress is a question of learning from past mistakes, of falsifying theories and putting up alternatives for criticism. All we ever have are provisional conjectures:

> Our science is not knowledge *(episteme)*: it can never claim to have attained truth, or even a substitute for it, such as probability.[5]

Yet again, Popper says

> The old scientific idea of episteme — of absolutely certain, demonstrable knowledge — has proved to be an idol. The demand for scientific objectivity makes it inevitable that every scientific statement must remain tentative for ever. It may indeed be corroborated, but every corroboration is relative to other statements which, again, are tentative.[6]

And, ironically, his conclusion is

> Only in our subjective experiences of conviction, in our subjective faith, can we be 'absolutely certain'.[7]

According to Popper, for a postulate to have the status of a scientific theory it should involve the repeatability of experiments (and hence be truly falsifiable) and should be predictive. On these grounds the main theories we put forward in the last chapter are not scientific theories at all! For example, cosmology is not repeatable because we cannot run the universe many times; and biological evolution is neither repeatable nor, arguably, predictive. Indeed Popper did not at first regard evolution and cosmology as scientific theories! He did, however, subsequently change his mind on this point.

It is certainly good to bear in mind these rather humbling criticisms of science when we hear extravagant claims being made.

In practice, scientists are more optimistic than Popper would have them. They believe that genuine progress is being made (witness the 'superb' theories of Penrose), and in the words of

Polkinghorne that they are achieving 'a tightening grasp of an actual reality'.[8] Polkinghorne knowingly embraces what most scientists unthinkingly assume — a 'realist' philosophical position: the world is really there and our scientific laws genuinely relate to it. This is in contrast to 'instrumentalist' and other views which see science as providing only convenient calculational procedures, with no necessary basis in reality: what matters is not the truth of scientific theories but their usefulness.

Polkinghorne's is however, a 'critical' realism. The qualification is necessary to take account of:

(i)   The provisional character of scientific theories as I have described.

(ii)   The peculiar nature of reality at the quantum level, that is to say, he wants to maintain the objective reality of an electron despite its inherent unpicturability, its wave/particle dual nature and the implications of Heisenberg's Uncertainty Principle (which we discuss briefly below).

(iii)   The rôle of personal judgment in science.[9]

We shall come to the rôle of judgment shortly but, in the mean time, let us note that what scientists are exercising here in taking a realist position is of course none other than faith! This faith comprises the following key aspects:

(i)   That there is order in the universe which it is open to rational enquiry to discover.

(ii)   That this order, and the laws of nature which describe it, persist in all parts of the universe at all times both past and future.

As Einstein put it, 'The most incomprehensible thing about the universe is that it is comprehensible'.

The magnitude of what is being assumed here should not be underestimated, for it is truly remarkable that these conditions should hold in the universe. A Christian would see in this order the reliability and faithfulness of God as creator and sustainer of the universe:

> 'While the earth remaineth, seedtime and harvest, and cold and heat, and summer and winter, and day and night shall not cease' (Genesis 8:22)

> 'He maketh his sun to rise on the evil and the good, and sendeth rain on the just and on the unjust' (Matthew 5:45).

> The validity of the same laws of nature in all parts of the universe at all times is indeed incomprehensible unless they derive from a single source (we come back to this point in Chapter 9).

Here is Einstein again on the scientist's religious feeling of awe before the universe:

> His religious feeling takes the form of a rapturous amazement at the harmony of natural law, which reveals an intelligence of such superiority that, compared with it, all the systematic thinking and acting of human beings is an utterly insignificant reflection. This feeling is the guiding principle of his life and work, in so far as he succeeds in keeping himself from the shackles of selfish desire. It is beyond question closely akin to that which has possessed the religious geniuses of all ages.[10]

It is interesting that it is in the Christian West, which saw God as the personal, creative and faithful intelligence behind the universe, that science has flourished from the seventeenth century onwards. The view that this is no accident has been cogently argued by a number of authors, notably Jaki[11] and Hooykaas[12], and recently it has been aired again by John Barrow.[13] We shall have more to say about this significant fact in the next chapter.

A further principle used in scientific method in which a similar sort of faith is exercised is that known as Occam's razor. This arises from the observation that the laws of nature are elegant and aesthetic, often expressed with beautiful and concise mathematical symmetry. Hence scientists will choose the simplest and most elegant explanation from competing alternative explanations of any phenomenon. For example, it is perfectly possible to view the earth as the centre of the solar system as did Ptolemy, but then, in order for their observed retrograde motions to be accounted for, the planets must orbit the earth in very complicated epicyclic paths. Copernicus's placing of the sun at the centre, with Kepler's elliptical planetary orbits, was much simpler and has been much more fruitful subsequently. Even Einstein made the mistake of failing to adopt the simplest possible formulation of his equations of motion of general relativity the first time round, one of the greatest regrets of his life. He was worried at the time that the only stable solutions, for the universe as a whole, of the equations with zero 'cosmological constant', were either an expanding or a contracting universe, rather than the steady state which a non-zero constant would give. Of course the expanding universe has since been observed.

As with order in the universe and its homogeneity in obedience to the laws of nature found on earth, there is no *a priori* reason why the principle of Occam's razor should be valid.

The great Cambridge physicist Paul Dirac, who unified special relativity and quantum theory and predicted the existence of antimatter, took an extreme view of the importance of elegance in a theory:

> It is more important to have beauty in one's equations than to have them fit experiment ... because the discrepancy may be due to minor features that are not properly taken into account and that will get cleared up with further developments of the theory ... It seems that if one is working from the point of view of getting beauty in one's equations, and if one has a really sound insight, one is on a sure line of progress.[14]

Einstein's search for beauty in scientific theories has been described by Banesh Hoffmann:

> When judging a scientific theory, his own or another's, he asked himself whether he would have made the universe in that way had he been God. This criterion may at first seem closer to mysticism than to what is usually thought of as science, yet it reveals Einstein's

faith in an ultimate simplicity and beauty in the universe. Only a man with a profound religious and artistic conviction that beauty was there, waiting to be discovered, could have constructed theories whose most striking attribute, quite overtopping their spectacular successes, was their beauty.[15]

Appeal to the 'rationality' of a theory, as against experimental evidence for it, has also been emphasized by Michael Polanyi. Thus the exercise of personal judgment and skill is involved in the critical evaluation of scientific theories, and the result of this he calls 'personal knowledge'. This contrasts with a 'positivist' view of science as solely concerned with providing a codification of empirical data.

Polanyi gives the example of special relativity, supposedly derived by Einstein following the Michelson-Morley experiment's demonstration that there was no relative motion of the earth with respect to the aether. In fact Einstein came by relativity largely through a consideration of Maxwell's equations of electromagnetism and the electrodynamics of moving media. Moreover, subsequent experiments by D C Miller seemed to demonstrate that there was indeed an aether drag! The scientific community was profoundly influenced by the beauty and rationality of relativity and simply assumed that there was an error in Miller's experiments![16] On hearing of Miller's experiments himself Einstein made his famous remark, 'Subtle is the Lord, but malicious He is not', subsequently engraved in the common room fireplace at Fine Hall, Princeton, and used by Abraham Pais in the title of his superb biography of Einstein.[17]

The fact that personal judgment plays an important rôle in scientific progress does not imply that the whole enterprise is therefore totally subjective. Theories must be put forward for the rational assent of peers, and predictions and experiment are of vital importance. Thomas Kuhn[18] has so exaggerated the personal element that it would seem that science ceases to be a rational activity. Kuhn describes periods of 'normal' endeavour in science, where the currently held laws are explored and applied in a variety of situations, punctuated by dramatic 'paradigm shifts' when the whole structure is superseded. Such a shift would be that from Newtonian to relativistic mechanics. While there is clearly some truth in this as a description of the way science progresses, Kuhn overplays not only the choice between paradigms as depending on the powers of persuasion of the protagonists, but the dichotomy between paradigms. After all, as Polkinghorne points out, Newtonian mechanics is a good approximation in all but exceptional circumstances (speeds approaching that of light), otherwise it would not have been held for so long.[19]

So we must get the element of personal judgment in perspective. Even so, this discussion does help us dispel the simplistic notion that science is inhuman in its objectivity, relying solely on experimental evidence, and assured in its results. It is perhaps closer to religion than one might at first have thought. To quote Popper again:

> I am inclined to think that scientific discovery is impossible without faith in ideas which are of a purely speculative kind and sometimes quite hazy; a faith which is quite unwarranted from the scientific view.[20]

The self-correcting process of science in action

Time travels in divers paces with divers persons.

(Rosalind, *As You Like It.*)

We now move on to discuss real scientific theories again in the light of the foregoing philosophical discussion, and we start by looking at how a process of self-correction is indeed at work, as Popper requires.

In physics in the twentieth century there have been two major developments in which old theories have been falsified and new theories have assumed their place, as Popper would envisage science progressing. These developments are among the finest achievements of the human intellect.

Towards the end of the nineteenth century physicists were beginning to think that their subject was effectively sewn up. All the theory was embraced in Newton's laws of motion and the electromagnetic theory of James Clerk Maxwell, and all that it remained to do was to measure the fundamental constants of physics ever more accurately. As Albert Michelson said, 'Physical discoveries of the future are a matter of the sixth decimal place.' Yet there were some niggling problems outstanding. One of these was the failure to detect the earth's motion through the 'aether', confirmed by the famous experiment of Michelson himself and Edward Morley, as mentioned above.

With the special and general theories of relativity Albert Einstein revolutionized our concepts of space and time. Einstein was concerned that all physical laws (both mechanical and those involving the propagation of light) should remain the same for observers in uniform motion relative to one another. By assuming this, and adopting the additional premise that the speed of light is the same regardless of the motion of the source, Einstein was able to deduce that measurements of length depend on speed, that time runs at different rates for different observers, and that the order in which events occur is also observer-dependent. Famously, the equivalence of mass and energy encapsulated in the immortal equation $E = mc^2$ also emerged from the theory.

The Michelson-Morley experiment was certainly consistent with special relativity even if the historical influence of it on Einstein is more complex than the impression given by standard textbooks.[21] Moreover, the bizarre predictions of the theory have been confirmed by countless subsequent experiments in the laboratory.

A subtle discrepancy which classical physics had failed to solve was the minute shift (43 seconds of arc per century) observed in the perihelion (point of closest approach to the sun) of the orbit of the planet Mercury. According to Newton's theory the orbit should be a pure ellipse in the absence of other planets, and after account was taken of the perturbation due to the other planets this small discrepancy was left. Einstein's general theory of relativity extended the validity of physical laws to observers accelerating relative to one another. It embraced the Principle of Equivalence, that gravitational forces cannot be distinguished from inertial forces (those artificial forces, like the centrifugal, introduced into Newton's equations to make them apply in accelerated frames of reference). The theory introduced the concept of a curved space-time, the curvature being caused by the matter within it, and it predicted that light no longer travels in straight lines. Its calculation of the perihelion shift in Mercury's orbit matched that observed exactly. The further prediction of the bending of light rays by the sun was precisely confirmed in an experiment during an eclipse of the sun in 1919 by English astronomer Sir Arthur Eddington.

Perhaps even more bizarre than time dilation, length contraction and curved space-time are the ideas of quantum mechanics, the second major revolution referred to above. Here classical physics predicted the collapse of an electron orbiting a proton onto that proton as electromagnetic energy is dissipated — all atoms would collapse in like manner. Experimentally, there was the problem of the photoelectric effect. One of the great achievements of nineteenth century physics was to show that light consists of electromagnetic waves, yet the photoelectric effect, in which light above a certain frequency (but not below that frequency) ejects electrons from a metal, showed that it behaved like particles.

The solution proposed by the quantum physicists — Planck, Schrödinger, Heisenberg and Dirac — to these problems involves energy only occurring in discrete quanta; the impossibility of mutually accurate measurement of the position and momentum of a particle (not through any constraint on one's measuring device, but because of 'the way the world is', to use Polkinghorne's phrase); the 'borrowing' of energy from the vacuum; and the notion that particles exist in a mixture of possible states until a measurement occurs. Given two electrons we cannot distinguish between them, unlike in classical physics where we can distinguish billiard balls, say; and measurement in one location influences measurements carried out in another a great distance away, as shown by a famous thought experiment due to Einstein and his colleagues Boris Podolsky and Nathan Rosen.

Schrödinger's contribution was an elegant mathematical equation for the evolution of a quantity, the wave function, describing the state of a system. Although the wave function itself evolves deterministically, the outcome of a measurement is calculated as a probability derived from the wave function. This will be important to bear in mind when we discuss in Chapter 9 the implications for Christian faith of living in a non-deterministic universe.

The amazing thing is that these extraordinary theories have indeed explained the anomalous observations and have gone on to make predictions of their own which have subsequently been verified experimentally. They have therefore superseded Newton's theory and constitute the presently accepted theories in accordance with Popper's criteria.

Cosmology and biological evolution revisited

How extremely stupid not to have thought of that!

(T. H. Huxley, on first reading Darwin's *Origin of Species*.)

We have seen earlier that neither cosmology nor biological evolution, the two planks of the scientific world view discussed in the last chapter, strictly qualify as scientific theories according to Popper's criteria (although Popper now allows them). Yet the Big Bang theory and the theory of evolution by natural selection are widely accepted among scientists. Why?

As we saw in the last chapter the Big Bang theory explains the fact that the universe is expanding. Clusters of galaxies are observed to be travelling away from each other at a speed proportional to their distance apart. We have seen in the current chapter that an expanding universe is a consequence of Einstein's equations of general relativity, applied to the universe as a whole, with no cosmological constant. Yet this is by no means enough for the theory to be accepted. For example Bondi, Gold and Hoyle in 1948 introduced the so-called 'steady-state theory' which was also able to explain the fundamental observation of an expanding universe. This theory was based on the 'perfect cosmological principle', the philosophical position that the universe looks the 'same' at all times and all places. In this theory matter is continuously created to fill the gaps as galaxies move apart.

It is often thought in the world at large that the steady-state and Big Bang theories are still equal competitors. However, the choice between these theories was settled in 1964 when Penzias and Wilson discovered the 3° absolute (-270° Centigrade) cosmic microwave background radiation (for which discovery they received the Nobel prize).[22] This radiation field was predicted from the Big Bang theory by Gamow as a natural consequence of the cooling of the universe from its hot initial state. What is important about this radiation is that it is in *equilibrium*, ie at a uniform temperature. At a time when the universe was much denser than it is today the interactions of photons of radiation with matter would lead naturally to this equilibrium. In contrast, there is no explanation about how such a radiation field could come into equilibrium in the steady-state theory, in which the universe is too sparse for interactions to take place.

Another distinction between Big Bang and steady-state theories is that the former predicts that galaxies were closer together in the past. Now, when we observe distant galaxies we are observing them *as they were* in the past since the light from them takes a finite time to reach us on earth. Therefore, if distant galaxies are more clustered, this also favours the Big Bang over the steady-state theory; and this is indeed what is observed.

The Big Bang theory has also been successful in predicting the abundances of chemical elements in agreement with observation. It will be recalled from the previous chapter that elements heavier than hydrogen are built up in the cores of stars by nuclear reactions. Now it turns out that only about one tenth of the observed abundance of helium can be manufactured in this way. However, conditions in the early hot, Big Bang also favoured nuclear reactions.

Calculations by Peebles, Wagoner, Fowler and Hoyle show that the helium produced does indeed correspond very closely with that observed in the universe today. We are talking about a process occurring when the universe was about 100 seconds old, its temperature a billion degrees and its density 10^{27} times that of today![23]

A similar argument to the above applies to deuterium, the heavy isotope of hydrogen. Again nuclear reactions in stars fail to make the quantity observed and calculations show that the amount observed can indeed be manufactured in the early universe. The calculation also puts a tight constraint on the present mean density of the universe, consistent with that calculated from the mass of galaxies.

Thus there are indeed compelling reasons for accepting the Big Bang theory. Of course there are still many unknowns, and controversies rage on various issues. For example, did the universe go through an ultra-rapid inflationary phase in its first 10^{-32} seconds, as postulated by American astrophysicist Alan Guth to explain the isotropy of the microwave background and the closeness of the density of the universe to the value which would cause a recollapse? Notwithstanding such questions, what we find is that the broad outline of the theory is well established and that problems and divergences of scientific opinion concern the details.

Moving on to the theory of evolution, again there is a great deal of misunderstanding among laymen, perhaps especially Christians, of its status. Such an eminent Christian apologist and evangelist as Canon Michael Green is still evidently happy to write: '... it is a theory that is unproven, full of missing links, and by no means universally accepted in the scientific community ...'[24] This contrasts strongly with what A. R. Peacocke, a biochemist as well as a Christian, says: '... let me stress that the proposition of evolution — that all forms of life, current and extinct, are interconnected through evolutionary relationships — is not in dispute among biologists'.[25] Here, of course, Richard Dawkins is right to say, 'No serious biologist doubts the fact that evolution has happened, nor that all living creatures are cousins of one another'.[26] What is striking about the evidence for the theory of evolution is that there are three independent strands which are all in agreement.

The first of these strands is palaeontology, the study of fossils, in which the anatomy of extinct creatures is studied. Here we find that fossils progress from simple structures to more complicated structures as the ages of the geological strata in which they are found decrease. The natural interpretation of this is that the more complex species have evolved from the simpler ones as time has advanced. The most recent fossils bear the greatest relationship to living species. Objections from Christians that there are many missing links in the fossil record look uncomfortable as more and more links between species are found. Such links include Archaeopteryx, between reptile and bird, found in Darwin's day, and links since found between fish and land vertebrates and between reptiles and mammals.[27] However, evolution could in fact be falsified if complex fossils were found in early rock strata. As Dawkins says, 'If a single, well-verified mammal skull were to turn up in 500 million year-old rocks, our whole modern theory of evolution would be utterly destroyed.'[28]

The second strand of evidence for evolution comes from taxonomy, the classification of living species of animals and plants via considerations of anatomy and morphology. I think it must have been to this branch of biology that Lord Rutherford was particularly referring when he made the rather derogatory remark, 'Science is divided into two categories, physics and stamp-collecting.' Nevertheless, this discipline has been extremely important in building up an evolutionary tree showing the relatedness of the various species.

The third evidential strand is molecular biology. This has studied the amino acid sequences in proteins with the same function in a wide variety of species. By examining the closeness of these sequences for the various species an evolutionary tree can again be constructed. For example the enzyme cytochrome-C in man consists of a sequence of 104 amino acids, of which only 1 is different in rhesus monkeys, 12 are different in horses and 22 are different in fish.[29] Moreover, we can go even further and use these differences as a biological clock to estimate the times when branching occurred in the evolutionary tree. For example, man and the apes branched their separate ways some 5 million years ago.[30]

As in cosmology, so in biology there have also been alternative theories to those currently held. Perhaps the most important historical contender in the biological field has been Lamarckism. This was first put forward by the French naturalist Jean Baptiste de Lamarck in 1809, some fifty years before the publication of The Origin of Species by Darwin. Lamarck believed that characteristics acquired during the lifetime of an animal could be inherited by its offspring. Combined with his 'principle of use and disuse' whereby organs that were exercised grew and those that were neglected withered, this provided a powerful explanation for how species might evolve. However, experiments show that the progeny of individuals which have undergone some change due to their environment do not in general develop those new characteristics. For example, flies which develop dumpy wings as a result of heat shock administered to them as pupae do not pass on dumpy wings to their offspring.[31] The so-called 'Central Dogma' of neo-Darwinism, that information flows from DNA to proteins and never the other way, is borne out by such experiments. And there have been some notable examples of fraudulent and failed attempts to prove otherwise.[32]

As we noted in Chapter 2, when Darwin formulated the theory of evolution by natural selection its genetic basis was unknown to him. We now know that genes undergo random mutations which may or may not be beneficial for survival, but that natural selection is responsible for perpetuating beneficial changes. The theory gives a powerful explanation for the origin of species, and for behaviour observed in nature today. As for cosmology, there is disagreement about the details (eg is evolution by slowly accumulating changes or does 'punctuated equilibrium', ie the existence of long periods of stability followed by rapid spurts of evolution, pertain?), but the fact of evolution is not in dispute among scientists.

Discussion

Every sentence I utter must be understood not as an affirmation but as a question.

(Niels Bohr.)

So what has our consideration of scientific method taught us? We have seen that science is not absolute and that its theories at any time are only provisional. This should already make us wary of claims to finality made in some of the popular books to which I referred in Chapter 1. Hawking and others should of course go on looking for the 'Theory of Everything' because of its importance for physics and cosmology, and the very search is scientifically rewarding and fruitful. But a cautionary note is in order. Theories of Everything, or at any rate complete and final theories of physics, have been with us before. Newton's theory of gravitation and his laws of motion were extraordinarily effective and powerful in predicting the behaviour of the heavenly bodies and of matter on the macroscopic terrestrial scale. With Maxwell's great synthesis of the laws of electromagnetism physicists thought their subject was complete, apart from refined measurements of the constants in the sixth decimal place. How wrong they were! The very concepts of space and time and even of causality were challenged, first by Einstein's theories of special and general relativity, and then by quantum mechanics. If we wanted we could go into other instances — for example, the idea that we had reached the ultimate building blocks of matter in the proton, neutron and electron was exploded (fairly literally!) when exotic new particles were discovered from the 1930s on. Perhaps the more sober wording of an earlier generation should be heeded:

> We are setting out to explain the approximation to the truth provided by twentieth century astronomy. No doubt it is not the final truth, but it is a step towards it, and unless we are greatly in error

it is very much nearer the truth than was the teaching of nine-teenth century astronomy.[33]

The word approximation is particularly important as we have seen. In deriving any scientific theory we have had to neglect certain aspects of reality, as we do when we apply such a theory to any new situation. Thus we can never be sure that the theory itself is anything but approximate. Exaggerated claims, based on Newton's laws of motion, that we live in a completely deterministic universe were thus always of dubious validity. This is a theme to which we shall return in Chapter 6.

The scientific method discussed above gives no warrant for reductionist assumptions — it is simply a rational method of enquiry for discerning the way things are. It does not tell us that all sciences are reducible to physics (though reducing phenomena to their component parts may well be helpful for investigative purposes). Neither does it encourage us to believe that a Theory of Everything is achievable, let alone that we are on the brink of discovering such a theory. Philip Lubin, an American astronomer on the COBE satellite team which made the recent very important discovery of fluctuations in the microwave background radiation, which many believe is a step towards a Theory of Everything, said: 'Every generation thinks it has the answer, and every generation is humbled by nature.[34]

Despite the qualifications that it is appropriate to apply to scientific theory, we have also seen that science 'works' in the practical sense that it is gaining a 'tightening grasp of an actual reality', in Polkinghorne's expression. Theories are indeed superseded, but the newer theories provide better and more general explanations of phenomena than their predecessors.

We have seen too that scientists in going about their business exercise a kind of faith. They rely on the order and rationality of the world. And it is very hard to see where this order and rationality, and the applicability of the same laws across all of space and time, could come from except there be a single source for them, namely God.

As a further point, intriguingly, modern quantum physics is showing more strongly than ever the unity of all natural things and the importance of the observer in the universe. A measurement made in one location is intimately linked to others great distances away. Moreover, no longer can we separate ourselves from supposedly objective natural phenomena in the old Cartesian manner, since merely by observing we affect the course of events.

The universe is open to rational enquiry. We, members of the species *Homo sapiens*, can delve into the mysteries of the atom and return with our minds and our equations to the smallest fraction of a second from the beginning of time. How come? It is very hard to see any 'survival value' in these esoteric abilities. Yet that is all a reductionist view has to offer. Surely it is more rational to believe that there is an ultimate Reason underlying not only the physical universe, but our own reasoning ability.

We now examine how such a belief in the ultimate Reason has lain behind the emergence of the scientific endeavour in the West and not elsewhere, and we grasp the nettle of the two great historical controversies which have bedevilled relations between faith and science.

CHAPTER 4

Where did this view come from? –
Historical Perspective

I see no good reason why the views given in this volume should
shock the religious feelings of anyone.

(Charles Darwin, *Origin of Species*, 1859.[1])

Lewis Wolpert asserts that 'religion and science are incompatible'.[2]
He is of course only the latest in a long line (including Richard
Dawkins, Peter Atkins and others whom we have encountered earlier) to express this view. In this chapter I want briefly to explore
some aspects of the historical relationship between science and religion, especially Western Christianity. I hope thereby to show that,
contrary to the opinions of Wolpert and others, modern science
owes its very development to an intellectual climate permeated by
Christian thought. Further, in looking at two major episodes in
the relationship between science and faith, I show how a mythology of conflict has developed entirely unjustified by the events to
which they relate.

It was indeed in Western Christendom that modern science ini-
tially took root and flourished. Was this merely accidental, or is
there some fundamental reason why Christendom should provide
the fertile soil in which the new ideas of science could spring up
and grow? What is it about the Christian faith that is conducive to
the scientific spirit of enquiry?

A fundamental tenet of Christianity (and the Judaism out of
which it grew) is surely the belief that the universe is the creation of an
omniscient and omnipotent Being. Furthermore, the vital properties

of the Judaeo-Christian God are that he is supremely good and infinitely loving — indeed 'God is love' (1 Jn 4:8,16).

We are told that God surveyed all that he had made and, 'behold, it was very good' (Gen 1:31). Very importantly, God had created the universe ex nihilo, in contradistinction to earlier Greek ideas that he moulded recalcitrant, pre-existent matter — indeed the maker, or rather moulder, of the world was referred to in Plato's Timaeus as the 'demiurge' from the Greek word for craftsman. The Christian view also contrasts with Plato's idea that real material objects are but the imperfect manifestation of perfect, heavenly 'forms'. On Plato's view it is the forms which are deserving of study (like Euclid's infinitesimally thin straight lines and perfect circles), not their manifestation in the material realm. In contrast again, the Christian idea that the world is contingent means that we have to look at the world itself to find out how it is made and functions. Because on this view the world could be otherwise than it is, the only way to find out how it is is to experiment! Pure logical reasoning, as exercised in Plato's Academy, will not get us there.

One is reminded of the amusing jibe at the Greeks made in modern times by Bertrand Russell:

> Aristotle maintained that women have fewer teeth than men; although he was twice married, it never occurred to him to verify this statement by examining his wives' mouths.[3]

It follows from the Christian view of God being good and loving that he is also trustworthy. This implies that we should expect to find a deep harmony in the natural order. We have already met Einstein's famous dictum, 'The most incomprehensible thing about the universe is that it is comprehensible'. Since mankind is that part of God's creation endowed with reason, and man is given 'dominion' over nature (Gen 1:28), it is to be expected that nature should yield to the application of man's reason. We should expect nature to display rationality and order, and for us not to be deceived when we seek out these qualities.

The kind of God Christians believe in would not plant fossils in the rocks in layers of increasing complexity to deceive us into believing that species have evolved over millions of years, if they had not done so; nor would he deceive us into thinking that galaxies were millions of light years distant and therefore existed millions of years ago, if that were not true. Going back to the sixteenth and seventeenth century controversies, observations of nature which indicate a heliocentric solar system, and elliptical planetary orbits, have to be taken seriously since God does not delude us when we explore his creation.

It is important to recognise that other philosophical and religious outlooks do not lead in the same direction as the Christian. On the Platonic view that intransigent matter was taken and moulded, one might expect unpredictable chaos rather than order. Science did not develop in the East whose mystical religions denigrate the material. In the West the material is the good creation of a holy and morally perfect God. In a polytheistic universe one could not expect the unity and harmony which the monotheistic Judaeo-Christian tradition would lead us to expect. We have seen that the universe obeys the same laws of physics in all places and at all times, or at least that it is very fruitful scientifically to assume this.

A pagan view in which nature is deified also does not lead to the experimentation which is necessary for science. On this view nature is too holy, rather than too lowly, for such exploration. The Christian view surely has the balance right. It is God who is worshipped and his creation reveals his glory.

Francis Bacon (1561-1626) was perhaps the most influential expounder of the view that nature is to be explored as God's creation. He saw that God had provided us with two books, Scripture and Nature. These books are the study material of two disciplines, namely theology and science. Moreover it is important to distinguish the two: in particular Scripture is not to be used as a textbook for science.

Bacon was deeply critical of the Greeks for their neglect of experiment, and was concerned to move away from the Aristotelian legacy which had been counted as authoritative through the middle ages:

> We will have it that all things are as in our folly we think they
> should be, not as it seems fittest to the divine wisdom, or as they
> are found to be in fact ... we clearly impress the stamp of our own
> image on the creatures and the works of God, instead of carefully
> examining and recognising in them the stamp of the creator
> himself.[4]

The seventeenth century was the great age of science, and the leading scientists were all Christian believers going about their business in just the way Bacon suggested. Let us just briefly mention two examples, Kepler and Newton.

Johannes Kepler (1571-1630) is famous for the discovery of his three eponymous laws of planetary motion. The most fundamental of these is that the planets orbit the sun not in circular but in elliptical orbits with the sun at one focus of the ellipse. This is revolutionary in breaking away from the long-held authority of the Greeks in holding to 'perfect' circles as the only possible orbits. By hypothesizing elliptical orbits Kepler was able to resolve the discrepancy in the observed motion of Mars compared with the prediction of the Copernican system.

Kepler was a man of deep Christian faith, believing that in his astronomical work he was 'following in God's footsteps after him'. He had been brought up a Lutheran and held fast to his faith through many trials. In a letter written in 1598 to Herwart von Hohenberg, the Catholic Chancellor of Bavaria, he declared, echoing Bacon, that astronomers, as priests of God to the book of nature, ought to keep in mind above all else the glory of God.[5]

The greatest of all scientists, Sir Isaac Newton (1642-1727), was also a Christian believer. He it was who discovered the law of gravity and the laws of motion, and from them derived Kepler's laws, thus completing the synthesis. In the preface to his great treatise *Philosophiae Naturalis Principia Mathematica* (1687) he wrote: 'Without all doubt this world ... could arise from nothing but the perfectly free will of God.'

He went on in the same passage to write of the 'many traces of the most wise contrivance' in nature and to criticize those who thought, like the Greeks, that they could discover how nature was through the exercise of reason alone.[6]

Newton also engaged in theological study. Indeed he thought this much more important than his work in science, though history has rightly judged otherwise. We shall consider later (in Chapter 10) how in one particular he combined his scientific and theological interests, in calculating the date of Christ's death, and came close to the view of modern astronomers and theologians.

One could go on cataloguing the Christian beliefs of the great scientists, but I want to turn instead to a different matter of vital importance. I am sure it would be thought disingenuous by many if I did not at least mention in this chapter what are popularly regarded as the two outstanding examples of supposed conflict between science and the church. These are of course the episodes involving Galileo and Charles Darwin. It is in fact very important to discuss these cases since there is a mythology attached to them in the popular mind. I shall therefore spend some time discussing each of these controversies. Since these are areas where there appears at least a *prima facie* conflict with the Bible, which after all is the foundation document of the Christian church, I end the chapter with a brief look at how the scientists themselves, and theologians, handle this issue.

The Galileo controversy

I beseech you that next after the Scriptures you study that great volume, the works and created objects of God, strenuously and before all books, which should only be regarded as commentaries.

(Francis Bacon, *Epistolae*, 6.)

For the bulk of my account of what follows I have drawn heavily on Arthur Koestler's masterly volume, *The Sleepwalkers*.[7] I do not think the basic facts which Koestler reports are in dispute: they are simply not widely known. A recent account by Oxford historian of science Allan Chapman certainly seems to confirm the story as told by Koestler.[8] There are a number of important points to bring out of the story of Galileo and the church.

In 1610 Galileo observed Jupiter and its four moons through his newly acquired telescope, and saw in the observation confirmation by analogy of Copernicus's heliocentric theory of the solar system.

While Galileo latched on to Copernicus's view that the sun is at the centre of the solar system, he actually had no real evidence or proof that this was the case. Indeed such evidence was not forthcoming for another two hundred years, when F. W. Bessel observed stellar parallax in 1838. You will remember from Chapter 2 that stellar parallax is the means by which the distances of the stars are measured, and relies on the motion of the earth relative to the stars — which is what the old Aristotelian view denied.

Furthermore, Copernicus's system was only marginally less complicated than that of Ptolemy, involving, just as did the latter, complicated epicyclic orbits (Arthur Koestler counts 48 epicycles compared with only 40 in Ptolemy![9]). In the Copernican system, the earth orbits a point some distance away from the sun and the planets orbit the same point in paths comprising epicycles on epicycles. The one great advantage of moving the hub to near the sun is that it solves the observed retrograde motion of the planets. However, it was left to Kepler, who postulated elliptic orbits for all the planets with the sun at one of the foci of the ellipse, to derive the correct system, and that in total accord with observation.

Copernicus's *De revolutionibus orbium coelestium* (Concerning the revolutions of the heavenly spheres) was published as long ago as 1543; Kepler's *Astronomia nova* appeared in 1609. The elliptical orbits gave a much more economical picture (in the Occam's razor sense) than Copernicus's system. Thus the latter was effectively out of date when Galileo took up the cudgels. Nevertheless, it was the Copernican view which Galileo espoused, possibly because of the rather arrogant attitude he displayed to his contemporary scientists, especially Kepler. Einstein, a gentler genius, was deeply saddened by Galileo's attitude: 'You know, it has always hurt me to think that Galileo did not acknowledge the work of Kepler,' he said.[10]

Other Catholic astronomers, especially the Jesuits, the intellectuals of the church, were very accommodating to Galileo's view! Indeed Galileo was fêted in Rome in 1611 when the Jesuits accepted the early telescopic findings, for example that the phases of Venus demonstrated that that planet orbited the sun. Most Jesuits officially held the cosmology of Tycho Brahe in which the planets orbited the sun but the sun in its turn orbited the earth, but many were 'closet' Copernicans. It is probably true to say that the heliocentric theory would have been quietly accepted by the church much sooner had it not been for the arrogance of Galileo.

Galileo himself seemed to go out of his way to manufacture trouble. The official church teaching was that the Copernican view could be held as a working hypothesis, but could not be proclaimed true unless incontrovertible proof were provided. Unless and until such proof were forthcoming the literal meaning of Scripture was to be upheld. The real target of such conservatism was of course, not the scientists, but the Lutherans, for all this was taking place in the aftermath of the Reformation.

Galileo's mistake was to enter the theological fray because he simply couldn't produce the astronomical proof required. For some years he was upheld in disputes by his friends among the cardinals. But he simply couldn't accept the compromise demanded by the church and insisted on forcing its hand.

So it was that in 1616 he was first brought before the Inquisition. The result was a decree condemning the Copernican hypothesis (watered down by pressure from the more enlightened cardinals, so that it was never declared a 'heresy'). In practical terms scholars were, however, left free to discuss it *ex hypothesi*, as before. Galileo was not mentioned in the decree, and, wishing to scotch rumours that he had been humiliated or punished, he obtained from Cardinal Bellarmine a certificate of the proceedings which did uphold him on these counts. He was, nevertheless, instructed by the cardinal that the doctrine of Copernicus could not be defended or held. However, produced at his trial in 1633 was a document which seemed to contradict this certificate by going further and stating that Galileo was formally forbidden 'to hold, teach, or

defend in any way whatsoever, verbally or in writing' the Copernican system.[11] The distinction is of vital importance. To this day it
is not clear whether the document ordering a total prohibition was
a forgery, though it does seem likely.[12] Of course Galileo did continue to espouse the Copernican theory.

It must be said that Galileo was at best incautious in the whole
affair surrounding his *Dialogue Concerning the Two Great World
Systems* which he published in 1632. First, he obtained the *impri-
matur* for the book by rather underhand means, even deceiving
Pope Urban VIII himself. Then, more seriously, the pope was popularly identified with the character Simplicius who put forward almost verbatim an argument of the pope's at the end of the book.
Simplicius was the fool in the book — clearly a buffoon. Every
argument he advanced was trounced, so one is led to believe that
Galileo thought the pope's argument false too. The pope had suggested to Galileo a way round the problem of arguing for the Copernican system without asserting it to be true — God may have
produced phenomena by entirely different means which are not
understood by human minds.[13] Yet Urban VIII and Galileo had
seemingly got on extremely well. It is almost as if Galileo were
going out of his way to antagonize his old friend.

The strident tone of the *Dialogue* was quite extraordinary. Anyone who did not agree with Galileo was a 'mental pygmy', 'dumb
idiot', 'hardly deserving to be called a human being'.[14] Yet, as
Koestler shows, Galileo's own arguments were weak and often plain
wrong. For example he put forward an erroneous theory of the
tides as justification for a moving and rotating earth, a theory which
even predicted only one high tide per day instead of two.

Galileo was summoned before the Inquisition for the second
time in April 1633. At his trial Galileo said that he did not believe
the Copernican theory and was not intentionally putting it forward in the *Dialogue*. He produced the certificate given him by
Cardinal Bellarmine, unfortunately now deceased, giving him permission to explore the Copernican theory as an hypothesis. He was
presented by the Inquisitor with the aforementioned suspect injunction of 1616 forbidding him to teach or hold the Copernican

position in any way. While Galileo did not recall these words of the injunction, he very foolishly pretended that the *Dialogue* did not say what it manifestly did say. For it was clear that the author of the *Dialogue* believed the Copernican system, and so the Inquisitors knew.

After the first hearing Cardinal Firenzuola, Commissary of the Inquisition, interviewed Galileo privately and suggested a course of action which might satisfy the Inquisition. The Commissary wrote that after many arguments he persuaded Galileo that he had gone too far in his book, and that Galileo asked for time to think how he would confess before the Inquisition. Two days after this interview Galileo was called before the Inquisition a second time and made his confession. This was to the effect that he had re-perused the *Dialogue*, which he had not read for three years, and found that he had placed arguments in favour of the Copernican hypothesis which came across much more strongly than he had intended, since his real intention was to refute rather than uphold Copernicus. He had not realized his own power of putting forward plausible arguments in favour of an hypothesis in which he did not believe.

Throughout the period of his trial Galileo lived in luxury un-precedented for a prisoner of the Inquisition. At no time was he confined to the dungeons. On the contrary, he lived in the Tuscan Ambassador's residence until the first hearing; then moved to a five-roomed flat in the Holy Office itself overlooking St Peter's and the Vatican Gardens; and then back to the Tuscan Embassy before the end of the trial, 'a procedure quite unheard of, not only in the annals of the Inquisition but of any other judiciary'[15]. The sentence decided upon 6 weeks later contained the statement that Galileo should

> ...abjure before a plenary assembly of the Congregation of the Holy Office, and is to be condemned to imprisonment at the pleasure of the Holy Congregation, and ordered not to treat further, in whatever manner, either in words or in writing, of the mobility of the Earth and the stability of the Sun.[16]

Furthermore, the *Dialogue* was banned and put on the Index of prohibited books. The pope, however, was concerned that 'he may suffer as little distress as possible, since matters cannot be let pass without some demonstration against his person'.[17]

At his third and last examination Galileo affirmed repeatedly under questioning that he had not held the Copernican opinion since he was forbidden to in 1616. He was indeed at this stage bidden to speak the truth under threat of torture, but this was merely a ritual formula: both sides knew Galileo was lying, yet the Inquisition clearly had no intention of breaking him.

'Prison' for Galileo comprised in turn the Grand Duke's villa at Trinità del Monte, Archbishop Piccolomini's palace in Siena, his own farm at Arcetri, and finally his house in Florence. He spent his remaining years working in the field of dynamics, his real area of expertise and that in which he made an enduring contribution.

Of course the Inquisition was wrong in condemning Galileo, even in its own terms, for the Catholic Church had never pronounced the Copernican system heretical. Yet Galileo was condemned as 'vehemently suspect of heresy'.[18] He was also condemned for breaking the 1616 injunction which, as we have seen, was of doubtful validity. I hope I have made it clear, however, that much of the blame for the whole affair must rest with Galileo himself, and that much of the popular mythology surrounding the affair is erroneous. We have seen that Galileo was not tortured, nor was he imprisoned in the dungeons of the Inquisition.

Galileo was a towering genius, yet a flawed genius. He went out of his way to make trouble when he had no proof of his claims. Time and again the authorities bent over backwards to support him until eventually he was just too provocative. His epitaph is the famous phrase *eppur si muove* ('but it does move') which he is supposed to have uttered at his trial, but never did.

As an interesting postscript to the whole affair, Koestler cites the spread of belief in the Copernican system to China and Japan from the end of the seventeenth century onwards by missionaries from none other than the Society of Jesus.[19]

The evolution debate

He bought white ties, and he bought dress suits,
He cramm'd his feet into bright tight boots,
And to start his life on a brand new plan,
He christen'd himself Darwinian Man!
He christen'd himself Darwinian Man!
But it would not do, The scheme fell through —
For the Maiden fair,
whom the monkey craved,
Was a radiant Being,
With a brain far-seeing —
While a Man, however well-behav'd,
At best is only a monkey shav'd!

(W S Gilbert, 'The Ape and the Lady' from *Princess Ida*, 1884.)

Turning to the dispute over evolution, the myth here undoubtedly centres round the famous confrontation between Samuel Wilberforce, Bishop of Oxford, and Thomas H. Huxley, 'Darwin's bulldog', at the British Association meeting held in Oxford in July 1860. Darwin himself was in fact rather shy of such public debates and was perfectly happy to leave evolutionary apologetics, at least in its public combative form, to his good friend Huxley.

The meeting was the first official function to be held at the new University Museum. The museum was the project of Henry Acland, Regius Professor of Medicine, a profoundly religious man who, like his predecessors in the sixteenth and seventeenth centuries, saw science as interpreting God's revelation in nature — he did much to establish the place of science in Oxford.[20]

What has passed into legend from the famous duel begins with Wilberforce's pointed question, whether it was on his grandfather's or his grandmother's side that Huxley claimed descent from an ape. At this point Huxley is reputed to have whispered to a neighbour, 'The Lord hath delivered him into mine hands'. When he delivered his own speech it contained the following riposte, as recorded here by himself:

> If then, said I, the question is put to me would I rather have a miserable ape for a grandfather or a man highly endowed by nature and possessed of great means and influence and yet who employs that influence for the mere purpose of introducing ridicule into a grave scientific discussion I unhesitatingly affirm my preference for the ape.[21]

The debate certainly needs to be put in context, for as Darwin's most recent biographers, Adrian Desmond and James Moore, put it:

> Thus it was that a witty bit of repartee on Saturday 30 June 1860, at a section meeting of the British Association for the Advancement of Science, was destined to be blown out of all proportion to become the best known 'victory' of the nineteenth century, save Waterloo.[22]

And again:

> Later legends depicted a bloody clash, with Wilberforce scotched if not slain.[23]

The first point to note is that, before Wilberforce rose to speak, the audience had suffered some two hours of intense boredom, mainly from the chief speaker, New York University professor J. W. Draper. Draper was one of the chief protagonists of the 'conflict myth' whose highly influential book *History of the Conflict between Religion and Science*[24] is now discredited.[25,26] However, he was despised even by Huxley. Thus, although Wilberforce's remark in the event was unfortunate, it was intended only as a joke to lighten proceedings after Draper's excesses.

Secondly, the accounts of the two great Darwinian protagonists at the meeting, the botanist Joseph Hooker and Huxley himself, are very different — each claimed victory over 'Soapy Sam', and Hooker in particular thought it was himself alone who secured the victory. Apparently the audience of the day was divided on the outcome and Wilberforce himself came away quite happy that he

had 'given Huxley a bloody nose'. Unfortunately there is no min-
uted record of the actual speeches, which is a great pity since so
much has been built on them.

Incidentally, Desmond and Moore argue that Wilberforce was
rather daring in proposing an ancestral ape for a grandmother in
view of 'Victorian sensibilities about the sanctity of the female sex'.[27]
They also cite geologist Adam Sedgwick's attack on an earlier Darwinian tract, *Vestiges of the Natural History of Creation* by Robert
Chambers (1844), as wishing to save 'our glorious maidens' from
'such depravity'![28] This throws an interesting light on the W S Gilbert quotation at the head of this passage!

It is perhaps not surprising that only the year after the publication of *Origin of Species* there was great debate about the issue,
especially among scientists, and that this should include eminent
churchmen who often, like Wilberforce himself, were distinguished
amateurs. Though it can scarcely be doubted that Wilberforce did
genuinely oppose the theory of evolution, Clifford Longley quotes
a rather more sober and scientifically impeccable review of the *Origin*
by Wilberforce himself:

> We have no sympathy with those who object to any facts or al-
> leged facts in nature, or to any inference logically deduced from
> them, because they believe them to contradict what it appears to
> them is taught by Revelation.[29]

This would accord well with the views of Bacon and, indeed,
Galileo. For the most part, in any case, the church had no problems with the theory of evolution by natural selection. That is to
say, there was no quarrel with the theory as providing an explanation for the development and existence of the various biological
species. I discuss below the specific question of the interpretation
of the early chapters of Genesis. As today, however, problems arose
if protagonists of Darwinism went on to claim that the theory had
removed purpose from the universe.

One important Christian thinker of the Victorian period who
saw clearly that there need be no contradiction between evolution
and the Christian faith was the Rev Charles Kingsley. Kingsley was

for most of his life Rector of Eversley in Hampshire, and also held the Regius Chair of Modern History at Cambridge from 1860 to 1869; he is well known as the author of *Westward Ho!*, *Hereward the Wake*, and *The Water Babies*. In particular Kingsley saw no reason to abandon natural theology, including the design argument of Paley and others, but rather saw that evolution gives us new insights into the same:

> We knew of old that God is so wise that He could make all things; but behold, He is so much wiser than even that, that He can make all things make themselves.[30]

Kingsley saw in the seeming 'chapter of accidents' of evolution rather the providential working of God. Professor Colin Russell quotes a particularly contemporary sounding passage from Kingsley's letters:

> Now they have got rid of an interfering God — a master magician, as I call it — they have to choose between the absolute empire of accident, and a living, immanent, ever-working God. ... Verily, God is great, or else there is no God at all.[31]

We shall return to discussion of the design argument and the question of how God might act in the universe in Chapter 9. In the mean time it is sufficient to note that Kingsley was far from alone (rather, his attitude could be described as the norm) in maintaining the traditional attitude of Bacon, Kepler and Newton in seeing both Nature and Scripture as revelations of God.

The 'episcopophagous' (bishop-eating) Huxley, however, had very different ideas from a synthesis of Darwinism with Christian belief. With Hooker and seven others, scientists and mostly Fellows of the Royal Society, he formed a secret association called the X-Club. The objects of the society were to promote science, and scientists as a profession, and to tear down the bastions of ecclesiastical authority and privilege. Their methods were unscrupulous: they did not forbear to propagate blatant distortions and untruths if it served their purpose. Thus it is to the X-Club and the historiographers who espoused their cause, especially Draper and later A. D. White, that we owe the myths that the church had opposed the use of chloroform in child-birth and the introduction of modern sanitation.[32] And to them also we owe much of the distorted picture we have of the Galileo story.[33,34] The X-Club managed to alter the election rules of the Royal Society to get their sympathizers elected[35] and also penetrated the British Association, Hooker and John Tyndall (see below) eventually becoming president.

The X-Club used Biblical metaphors to describe their aims. Their object was to 'smite the Amalekites' in the church (and science, too, where they met opposition), but even more seriously, science was to become a kind of substitute religion. Its temple was that great Victorian Gothic masterpiece, Waterhouse's Natural History museum — they called it 'Nature's cathedral'. They even went so far as to organize a Sunday Lecture Society, an imitation Sunday school, with lectures on science as a substitute for religious instruction. A 'Hymn to Creation' was sometimes sung at these meetings. They held mass, pseudo-evangelistic rallies, attempting to rival such great (authentic) evangelists of the time as Charles Spurgeon. Huxley referred to his speeches as 'lay-sermons' or even 'my preachment'[36] so that it is no wonder he earned the soubriquet 'Bishop Huxley' and his followers were dubbed a 'priesthood' and the 'church scientific'.

The X-Clubbers' philosophy was 'scientific naturalism', a reductionist creed which denied the supernatural and asserted that 'there is but one kind of knowledge and but one method of acquiring it'.[37] Their physics was deterministic, billiard ball Newtonianism, their biology, of course, evolutionary. All out war was declared on religion, and Desmond and Moore quote Huxley as warning that science had 'no intention of signing a treaty of peace with her old opponent, nor of being content with anything short of absolute victory and uncontrolled domination' over theology.[38] Desmond and Moore also describe the development of the X-Club's religious metaphors, for example its retaining a scientific hell for unbelievers in the physical gospel. John Tyndall, one of the X-Clubbers even advocated a new creed — 'I believe in one Force'.[39] Tyndall, who was a physicist, also hoped that physics would eventually solve the mind-body problem by identifying mind and brain (a question we return to in Chapter 7). However, even Huxley was sceptical about this, quipping 'Given the molecular forces in a mutton chop, deduce Hamlet or Faust therefrom.'[40] Tyndall's objective was described in his presidential speech to the British Association in Belfast in 1874:

> We claim, and we shall wrest, from theology the entire domain of cosmological theory. All schemes and systems which thus infringe upon the domain of science must, in so far as they do this, submit to its control and relinquish all thought of controlling it.[41,42]

It is interesting that Huxley and his followers did not abandon religion as such, only orthodox Christianity; they replaced it with the old paganism, the deification of Mother Nature. Also in Tyndall's speech quoted above was a commendation of the Renaissance mystic Giordano Bruno's view that matter is not that 'mere empty capacity which philosophers have pictured her to be, but the universal mother who brings forth all things as the fruit of her own womb'.[43] This pantheistic view of nature has its parallels today which we discuss in Chapter 8.

Huxley and his companions were opposed just as much from within the scientific establishment as by the church. In particular there was the eminent group of physicists, many of Scottish descent, and mostly at Cambridge, who held orthodox Christian views and did not see their science in opposition to their faith. These included James Clerk Maxwell, William Thompson (Lord Kelvin), Sir George Stokes and others. Thus Maxwell rejected the materialism of the scientific naturalists and, rather, recommended the pursuit of science as enlarging one's concept of the glory of God. Kelvin still held to the design argument of Paley, being unable to accept that life arose as a 'fortuitous concourse of atoms'.[44] Like Kingsley, he saw God as 'maintaining and sustaining His creation through the exercise of His Will'.[45] He criticized evolution from a scientific point of view, having calculated himself the age of the earth (about 100 million years) and this being too short for evolution to take place. The calculation did not take account of the then unknown source of heat generated by radioactivity, so his calculation was wrong. However, Darwin was worried by this and reacted rather desperately by incorrectly postulating higher rates of variation and even Lamarckian inheritance of highly used organs.

The judgment of Colin Russell is an excellent summary of the X-Club and its achievements:

> In their bitter battles for scientific hegemony the Victorian scientific naturalists fought largely in vain. But in establishing their myth of an enduring conflict between religion and science they were successful beyond their wildest expectations.[46]

Science and the Bible

The abnegation of reason is not the evidence of faith but the confession of despair.

(J. B. Lightfoot.[47])

We have seen that the great figures of the 17th century revolution in science were Christians and that the idea that there is a conflict between science and Christian faith is a myth largely invented in the nineteenth century by T. H. Huxley and his followers. There is still, however, the problem of the Bible, for on the face of it science does seem in fundamental conflict with Biblical teaching.

Richard Dawkins caricatures the religious as belonging to one of three categories: the 'no-contests', the 'know-nothings' and the 'know-alls'.[48] The 'no-contests' are sophisticates who get round the problems of revelation by saying simply that religion and science are about different things and therefore there can be no conflict. Dawkins regards them as dishonest, and their ideas of God as vague and without evidence. The 'know-nothings' are the fundamentalists who maintain that Scripture does provide a true cosmology, and religion an explanatory framework in competition with science. He regards these as 'in one way more honest', being 'true to history', but of course intellectually completely discredited. Finally the 'know-alls' simply think that religion is good for you but its objective truth an irrelevancy.

This is a ludicrously simplistic account. I shall be discussing further in later chapters both the sense in which religion enters the field of explanation and also how its subject matter is different from that of the natural sciences. But in the mean time let us return to the question of Scripture.

It would appear, as Dawkins claims, that both science and the Bible present a cosmology. Thus, while the existence of God can be neither proved nor disproved, and many other religious claims seem to be matters of belief which are inherently untestable, surely here the territory is common to both science and faith; and the creation story of Christianity is in blatant conflict with that of science. We have seen how first the Newtonian synthesis with the sun at the centre of the solar system, and in modern times the Big Bang theory, and the theory of biological evolution originating in the nineteenth century but only properly explained with twentieth century discoveries in genetics, have amassed a weight of evidence in their favour. So what about the stories of Genesis?

I shall return to the stories of Genesis 1-3 specifically in a moment, but first let us recall how Francis Bacon saw both Nature and Scripture as revelations of God. Kepler and Galileo took the same view and did not believe that the Bible was to be used as a scientific textbook, but that it used the language of the common man in talking of the sun rising and setting and so on. We still use such language, though we are well aware that it is the earth moving, not the sun.

Thus Galileo pointed out that the Bible was written in language 'according to the capacity of the common people who are rude and unlearned'.[49] If this were not so, and one had to take the Bible everywhere literally, then for example

> it would be necessary to ascribe to God feet, hands, and eyes, as well as corporeal and human affections, such as anger, repentance and hatred, and sometimes the forgetting of things past, and ignorance of things to come ...[50]

Conversely, regarding the purpose of the Scriptures, he said:

> The intention of the Holy Ghost is to teach us how one goes to heaven, not how heaven goes.[51]

Galileo invoked in his defence the great St Augustine, quite correctly (as we shall see below), but somewhat unfortunately for him since at that time Augustine's views were controversial on another subject (pre-destination).

Kepler too thought that the Scriptures were addressed to both 'scientific and ignorant men', and would therefore speak with the 'senses that are human'.[52] He discussed several Biblical passages. For example, in Psalm 19 the sun is likened to a 'bridegroom coming out of his chamber', running a race, and we read that 'His going forth is from the end of heaven, and his circuit unto the ends of it'; in Psalm 24 we read that the earth is 'founded upon the seas'; and Psalm 104 speaks of God stretching out the heavens like a curtain, laying the 'beams of his chambers in the waters', and the like. Kepler's assertion is that these passages are not about physics which would be to make a fool of the Holy Spirit, but speak in a poetic way about God's providence and his glory, and man's place in creation.[53]

This approach is in accord with the attitude of the Reformers and it is particularly worth mentioning Calvin here. Another of the myths propagated in the nineteenth century, by A. D. White, was that Calvin opposed Copernicus in his Commentary on Genesis. Calvin allegedly cited Psalm 93:1, 'the world also is stablished, that it cannot be moved', and went on to ask, 'Who will venture to place the authority of Copernicus above that of the Holy Spirit?' In fact there is no such passage in the commentary. The nearest we get to anything like this is a remark in a sermon on 1 Cor 10:19-24, that a moving earth conflicts with common sense — there is no mention of a conflict with Scripture, the passage being preached on has no cosmological implications, and Copernicus is not mentioned.[54]

Rather, Calvin developed a sophisticated 'accommodation theory' to explain that Scripture was not given for scientific instruction. As Hooykaas says, 'Calvin's exegetical method was based on the Reformation doctrine which held that the religious message of the Bible is accessible to everybody ... the Bible was "a book for laymen"; "he who would learn astronomy and other recondite arts, let him go elsewhere" '.[55] The accommodation theory said that the Holy Spirit would accommodate himself to vulgar errors in scientific matters, or indeed other factual and historical matters of little importance, in order to get across the spiritual message. So again, the waters 'above the firmament' (Gen 1:7) are not to be taken as meaning that there are oceans in the heavens, but rather, common-sensically, they are to be interpreted as clouds.[56] In all this Calvin exhibits a rather modern view of Biblical exegesis (see Chapter 10).

Moving on explicitly to the early chapters of Genesis, the view of modern professional theologians is that to regard these stories as scientific statements of how the world began is a profound mistaking of the kind of literature the Bible, and in particular the book of Genesis, is. In taking this view, they are following an historical tradition of exegesis from within the church — I have mentioned Calvin explicitly and will discuss still earlier traditions below.

This non-literal interpretation is also the view of someone who comes to the documents as an expert on world literature, C. S. Lewis, the great Christian apologist. The purpose of the Biblical writers is not to convey details of physics, nor could they have done so; and even if they could their readers would not have been able to understand! No, the purpose of the Bible writers is to convey God's ways to man. They do this in many ways — through historical narrative, through poetry, through song, through saga, and through mythical and legendary stories (in particular the genre of Jewish *midrash*, stories with a message). Always the purpose is the same: 'all scripture is given by inspiration of God, and is profitable for doctrine, for reproof, for correction, for instruction in righteousness' (2 Tim 3:16). To repeat, its purpose is not to provide us with a scientific textbook, however curious we may be about such matters.

The early chapters of Genesis are in fact among the most important in the Bible, in that they set the scene for all that follows. They will recur several times in our deliberations, but for the moment, briefly, their teaching is thus: God is creator; man is the pinnacle of creation put in charge of the natural world as God's steward; man has disobeyed God and embarked on his way of autonomy and separation from God.

To treat these chapters, particularly those dealing with the Garden of Eden story, as allegorical and not literal in no way detracts from an understanding of them as the inspired word of God. I say this for the benefit of those Christians who are involved in what to me is a futile battle to defend them as literal accounts. Sadly, I believe such attempts are damaging rather than helpful to the Christian cause. Moreover, they represent (despite what Richard Dawkins says) only a relatively recent, fundamentalist trend in understanding the Bible.

The early church fathers certainly tended to treat the Genesis stories allegorically, eg St Jerome described the early chapters of Genesis as written in the manner 'of a popular poet'.[57] And in his *Confessions* St Augustine describes (Book VI) how he learnt from Saint Ambrose 'how to interpret the ancient Scriptures of the law and the prophets in a different light from that which had previously made them seem absurd, when I used to criticize your saints for holding beliefs which they had never really held at all.'[58] He tells how Saint Ambrose 'disclosed the spiritual meaning of texts which, taken literally, appeared to disclose the most unlikely doctrines'. In Book XIII of *Confessions* Augustine gives some of his own detailed allegorical interpretations of the early chapters of Genesis, eg of the light created on the first day as representing the spiritual creation which became light by the reflection of God's glory, the darkness representing the soul still without God's light, the firmament representing the Scriptures providing a shield over us for our protection, and so on.

While we may now regard some of these interpretations as fanciful, nevertheless it is instructive to see how differently the Scriptures have been interpreted down the ages. Perhaps Augustine offers a lesson for modern, scientifically educated man who sees the text only in a narrow, literal sense and who then goes on to reject a chimera, a false view of his own making, which is no part of Christian belief anyway or certainly not a necessary part.

In fact there are two accounts of creation in Genesis, the first running from Chapter 1, verse 1, and the second beginning at Chapter 2, verse 4. The second story, which deals with the Garden of Eden, is in fact inconsistent in terms of the order of creation with Genesis 1 — a good enough reason in itself to believe that these chapters are not meant to be taken literally but to convey different messages. Different authors probably set them down in any case, following hundreds of years of oral tradition.

Genesis Chapter 1 tells us that God is the author of all things and that his creation is good; man is the pinnacle of that creation. From the fact that they are God's creatures, it follows that objects within creation like the greater and lesser lights (sun and moon) are not to be worshipped — an important message to an Israel surrounded by paganism, and an important message too to nineteenth century scientific naturalists and their twentieth century counterparts who wish to deify nature.

The message of the Garden of Eden story in Chapters 2 and 3 is surely that there is some selfish quirk in man's nature — original sin if you like — which affects his relationship with God, and ultimately means that he needs the redemption which Christ alone brings. And as we shall discuss in more detail in Chapter 7, this is in accord both with the 'selfish gene' picture of modern Darwinian evolution and of the insights of modern psychology. The story of Adam is the story of everyman, for indeed Adam means 'man'.

Summary

Biblical interpretation does not rely on a narrow literalism; long before the development of modern science great Christian saints like Augustine realized that non-literal interpretations were necessary to make sense of the Biblical stories. The message of the Bible is fundamentally a spiritual one, not a scientific one. Thus there is no need for there to be any conflict between science and faith on the grounds of cosmology or anthropology.

The great revolution in science took place in Western Christendom for very good reasons, and the leaders in that revolution saw themselves as finding out God's laws. The perception of conflict is a myth largely generated by scientific naturalists and their sympathetic historiographers in the nineteenth century. Most Christians were not discomfited by Darwinism as a theory of origins. Only when the denial of purpose in the universe is maintained as integral to the theory does it become a threat to spiritual values. And the validity of so maintaining is what we must examine in subsequent chapters.

CHAPTER 5

The Fallacy of Nothing-Buttery

The belief that a unified Theory of Everything will explain the structure of the Universe uniquely and completely will appear unashamedly in scientific papers, but it is essentially a religious or metaphysical view, in the sense that it rests only upon an unstated axiom of faith.

(John Barrow.[1])

It is time that we examined nothing-buttery (reductionism) in more detail. So far we have used the term somewhat loosely to denote a number of inter-related ideas — that scientific explanations are the only valid ones, that higher level sciences can be reduced to lower ones, and perhaps most fundamentally to the notion that we as human beings are 'nothing but' chance agglomerations of atoms and molecules which have been sifted and refined through natural selection.

Writers on this subject generally recognise three ways in which the term reductionism is used[2,3,4] and it is, therefore, worth qualifying the term accordingly. The three categories are: *methodological reductionism, epistemological reductionism* and *ontological reductionism.*

These are rather ugly and somewhat forbidding names for what turn out to be quite simple ideas. Thus methodological reductionism means breaking objects into their constituent parts in order to study them; epistemological reductionism denotes the notion that higher level sciences are explicable in terms of lower level ones; and ontological reductionism means that a scientific explanation for any phenomenon is the *sole* explanation. We examine each of these aspects in turn.

81

Methodological Reductionism

Sweet is the lore which Nature brings;
   Our meddling intellect
Misshapes the beauteous forms of things:–
   We murder to dissect.

(William Wordsworth, *The Tables Turned.*)

Methodological reductionism is essentially a research strategy and is accordingly hardly to be quarrelled with from the metaphysical point of view. By breaking the object of study into its constituent parts knowledge and insight have often been gained. Arthur Peacocke gives as an example a procedure he used to carry out as a physical biochemist before he turned to theology, viz. the isolation of the DNA molecule, in which the original biological entities (herring roes) were ground up, filtered, put into solution, and finally freeze-dried to obtain the DNA.[5] The process is plainly destructive, yet immensely fruitful. Clearly we do not want to deny that something of great value can be learned about the natural world from such procedures.

Nevertheless, despite the great success of methodological reductionism, it is also important to realize that a more holistic methodology is often necessary to understand natural phenomena — in classical terms we need both analysis and synthesis. The one approach is not right and the other wrong, rather the two are complementary to one another. Peacocke cites even strong reductionists such as Francis Crick (who in 1953, with James Watson, famously unravelled the structure of the DNA molecule) as recognising, besides the need to break up a cell and study its components, the complementary need to study the cell as a living unit to see what it does, one reason being that the breaking-up process itself might lead to spurious effects.[6]

In physics too there is increasingly a recognition that a holistic approach is necessary to balance the traditional method of isolating the object of study and smashing it to pieces, or at any rate that methodological reduction does not tell the whole story. The Einstein-Podolsky-Rosen (EPR) experiment shows that correlations exist between particles separated by great distances, and we also know that an observer cannot be truly isolated from his object of study. The leading proponent of such a holism is David Bohm, late Professor of Theoretical Physics at Birkbeck College, London. Commenting on these findings of quantum theory, he has this to say:

> A centrally relevant change in descriptive order required in the quantum theory is thus the dropping of the notion of analysis of the world into relatively autonomous parts, separately existent but in interaction. Rather, the primary emphasis is now on undivided wholeness, in which the observing instrument is not separable from what is observed.[7]

He goes on to say that relativity theory also exhibits a wholeness, different from that of quantum theory, in which the instruments of observation are modelled as 'singularities in the field'.[8]

We shall return to the findings of modern physics in Chapter 6 since they are relevant to all forms of reductionism.

Epistemological Reductionism

> The ultimate aim of the modern development in biology is in fact to explain *all* biology in terms of physics and chemistry.
>
> (Francis Crick.[9])

Epistemological reductionism is the name given to the idea that one science or theory can be reduced to another that is in some way more fundamental. Typically this is taken to mean that biology can be explained in terms of chemistry and chemistry in terms of physics. The hierarchy of sciences can be extended further so that sociology is explained in terms of the psychology of individuals and psychology in terms of biology; and theology, in so far as it represents a human need for God, can be explained in terms of sociology and psychology. It can also be extended by including 'in-between' sciences such as biochemistry. Ultimately the most fundamental science, physics, is explained in terms of its most fundamental entities (quarks and gluons?) and these in turn are described by mathematics.

A number of questions arise regarding the programme of epistemological reductionism. For example, what does it mean to say that one science or theory within a science has been reduced to another? More importantly, does the programme work— have any of the reductions actually been made, and, if not, is there any reason to suppose that they might be? Let me give examples of what are generally regarded as successful reductions.

Perhaps the paradigm successful reduction is that in physics of thermodynamics (the study of heat) to statistical mechanics. The laws relating the pressure, temperature and volume of a gas (the reader may remember Boyle's law, for example, from school physics) relate to properties of the gas at the macroscopic, everyday scale. If we imagine the gas to be composed of individual particles randomly colliding according to Newton's laws of motion (which I quoted in Chapter 3), and we make the connecting step of identifying the mean kinetic energy of the particles with the gas temperature, then the gas laws can be derived from Newton's laws. In a very real sense, we have here reduced macroscopic laws of a higher level science (or, strictly, sub-science, ie thermodynamics) to those of the interactions of particles.

Yet, even here at the heart of the archetype for successful reductions, there is a very big surprise in store. Thermodynamic systems exhibit irreversibility — the well known law that the amount of disorder in a system, as measured by the quantity known as entropy, increases with time. In contrast, however, Newton's laws of motion are reversible in time — the laws governing particle motion are symmetric in time so behaviour could go either way, whereas the laws of thermodynamics have a definite direction, or arrow, for time. The arrow of time is a fundamental property of the higher level science which cannot be derived from the lower level one. As an example, a cup knocked off a table will fall to the floor and disintegrate; we do not see broken cups reconstituting themselves and flying up to lie on table-tops — yet the equations at the particle level do not differentiate between the two possibilities.

It is often blithely assumed that the reduction of chemistry to physics is a *fait accompli*. The example of the chemical valency of the elements is perhaps a good one to take to see what is meant here. The way in which atoms combine to form molecules is determined by the 'valency' or combining power of the particular elements concerned. More precisely, the valency of an element is the number of chemical bonds that can be formed by an atom of that element, eg 1 for hydrogen, 2 for oxygen and 4 for carbon, giving rise to the molecular formulae H_2O (water), CH_4 (methane), and so on. Valency was originally explained, in the Bohr model of the atom, in terms of the number and arrangement of electrons, in the outer shells of the atoms, which are transferred or shared to form chemical bonds. We can now explain the structure of these shells in turn using quantum mechanics. Electrons as individual particles are replaced by electron clouds of certain allowed shapes and the shells are filled according to the allowed values of 'quantum numbers' representing the energy, angular momentum and so on of the electrons, to build up the periodic table of the elements. As with the thermodynamics example, however, all is not clear cut here either, since approximations are required in solving the quantum mechanical equations in order to derive the description of molecular structure.

Sir Karl Popper, as ever, has some very interesting things to say on this subject. In fact he sees all such reductions as incomplete:

> There is almost always an unresolved residue left by even the most successful attempts at reduction.[10]

In discussing chemical bonds Popper quotes Linus Pauling, author of *The Nature of the Chemical Bond*, as admitting to being unable to define precisely what this nature was. Notwithstanding this, Popper goes on to say that, even if we had a completely successful reduction in the terms I have outlined it would not be complete. This is because, first, the very existence of the elements we are talking about is dependent on introducing a theory of evolution into physics — cosmology, the Big Bang, nucleosynthesis in stars, supernovae explosions and so on, as I have described in Chapters 2 and 3. As I also indicated in Chapter 3, Popper regards cosmology as 'an almost borderline case of physical science'.

Secondly, Popper sees the generation of the periodic table as dependent on *preestablished harmonies* in nature (the phrase is Leibniz's). Thus the nuclear fusion of hydrogen nuclei occurs only in conditions of extreme temperature and pressure very rare in the cosmos. Further, these conditions are brought about when the extremely weak force of gravity is sufficient to overcome the electrical repulsion of the nuclei.[11] As we shall see in Chapter 9 when we discuss the anthropic principle developed by cosmologists, the universe is full of such preestablished harmonies: the universe is in fact very 'finely tuned' to bring about life.

Ernest Nagel[12] has formulated two criteria to be met for a successful reduction of one science or theory to another, viz *connectability* of definitions and *derivability* of laws. Thus, if we can define all the technical terms of the higher level science in terms of those of the lower (connectability), and then show that the laws of the former are logical deductions from those of the latter (derivability), then a successful reduction has been achieved. Nagel further refines the nature of the connections made, identifying three possibilities: (i) that they are purely logical connections; (ii) that they are conventions stipulated by fiat; or (iii) that they are factual or material.

In the thermodynamics example, we can define temperature in terms of mean molecular kinetic energy (connectability) and then derive the gas laws from Newton's laws of motion (derivability). Nagel discusses this example in some detail, particularly the nature of the connection between the classical notion of temperature, derived from readings of mercury thermometers, thermo-couples and the like, and the kinetic energy of molecules. It is clearly not a simple logical connection, since the two concepts are quite different, but it could be either of (ii) or (iii) above. I am sure that in practice physicists would regard the connection as factual, believing that if you measure a gas's temperature and the mean kinetic energy of its molecules the required proportionality would be found. The point is, though, that it is no mean feat to measure the kinetic energy of molecules, in contrast to temperature measurement, and so verify the connection as material.

In a similar way to the above we can define chemical valency in terms of the number of electrons in the outer orbitals of an atom and derive this number by (essentially) solving Schrödinger's equation in quantum mechanics. Again, I am sure chemists and physicists would regard the connection as a material one. So, notwithstanding the problems mentioned earlier, we can at least say that we have achieved a partial reduction of thermodynamics to the physics of particles and chemistry to quantum physics.

As has been pointed out by S. A. Barnett, even accepting without qualification that we have achieved the reduction of chemistry to physics in the sense described above, we have not thereby put the chemists out of business:

> The properties of substances in which atoms are combined to form molecules still had to be investigated in their combined form; for the new physics did not, and does not, tell us what these properties are. Even water, seemingly a very simple substance made of hydrogen and oxygen, has many complex features — among them, the various crystalline structures of snow. The study of hydrogen and oxygen, each in isolation, does not tell us what all their properties will be when combined. The findings of physics do not replace those of chemistry.[13]

When it comes to the reduction of biology to chemistry and physics the position is not nearly so hopeful for the reductionist cause as in the cases cited. Certainly, nothing like a comprehensive reduction is anywhere near being achieved. Thus F. J. Ayala:

> It is clear that in the current state of scientific development a majority of biological concepts such as cell, organ, Mendelian population, species, genetic homoeostasis, predator, trophic level, etc., cannot be adequately defined in physicochemical terms. Nor are there at present any classes of statements belonging to physics and

chemistry from which every biological law could be derived. That is, neither the condition of connectability nor the condition of derivability is satisfied. These considerations make it clear that the reduction of all or even most of biology to the physicochemical sciences is premature at present.[14]

Supremely, perhaps, natural selection is not a physical concept, nor is it reducible to physics. As Donald T. Campbell says:

Biological evolution in its meandering exploration of segments of the universe encounters laws, operating as selective systems, which are not described by the laws of physics and inorganic chemistry, and which will not be described by the future substitutes for the present approximations of physics and inorganic chemistry.[15]

What we do meet, however, in moving from a study of simple to more complex systems are the twin phenomena of *emergence* and *downward causation*.

The phenomenon of emergence is of fundamental importance to the debate about reductionism. What is meant by it is that, as we move to higher and higher levels of complexity new phenomena are discovered which could not have been predicted on the basis solely of structural decomposition, and which require their own language and terminology to explain them. This language and terminology, as well as the higher level laws relating concepts, are irreducible to those which apply to lower levels in the hierarchy of sciences and theories. Emergence is the other side of the coin from the failure of epistemological reductionism.

Even in the simple example of a mechanical device it is not clear that reduction works — rather, even here, emergent properties occur. Such a device consists of many components, which can of course be studied individually, and the relationships between parts can also be studied. Yet it is impossible to discover the *purpose* of the machine in this way. It is indeed absurd to say that the device consists solely of its individual parts. New meaning and purpose, requiring new language (describing the function of the machine), come about with the organization of the parts, in this case by a human being, into the whole. We might for example be talking about a type-writer — the idea of a letter or book is not reduced to the mechanical parts of the type-writer.

Yet, for the machine, although the parts have been arranged for some higher level purpose by a human engineer, it would seem that, by applying the laws of physics to the parts and noticing the geometrical arrangement and inter-relationships of the parts, we might actually be able to deduce the behaviour (we could predict what would happen to a type-writer if certain keys were pressed, though not the meaning of what was written). Polanyi makes the further point that physicochemical investigation of the machine, say in the event of failure, is only meaningful in the light of a knowledge of the machine's purpose or what he calls the 'operational principles' designed to bring about that purpose. But, as he insists, physics and chemistry are powerless to tell us what those operational principles are.[16]

In the natural world, this sort of prediction is much less likely to be possible. The idea of 'wetness' of water, for example, has no meaning at the level of a few water molecules but requires an aggregation of many molecules. Wetness is an 'emergent' property of water, not deducible solely from the molecular structure.

When it comes to biological entities, emergence is the norm and reduction ever less possible. Peacocke, following Polanyi, gives the example of the DNA molecule. Its structure is explicable in terms of the celebrated double helix: in particular we have a sequence of bases joined by chemical (covalent) bonds attached to a second sequence by other chemical (hydrogen) bonds, particular bases always attaching to their complement. In physicochemical terms any sequence of base pairs is allowable. However, in any particular cell of a given organism, a particular sequence will have a meaning for that organism in that it constitutes a set of coding instructions for manufacturing a particular protein. As Peacocke says:

> The concept of 'information transfer' which is needed to understand what is going on biologically when DNA functions in an actual cell cannot be articulated in terms of the concepts of physics and chemistry, even though the latter explain how the molecular

machinery (DNA, RNA and enzymes) operates to convey information. For the concept of 'information' is meaningless except with reference to the functioning of the whole cell, itself conceived in relation to its genetic and evolutionary history.[17]

'Information transfer' is thus an emergent property arising when that degree of complexity associated with cells and organisms is reached in the evolutionary process. And of course, when we come to man himself we have the emergence of consciousness, with the associated language of love, beauty and reason which is appropriate for that supremely complex organization of cells which is the human brain.

To accept emergence and deny epistemological reductionism is not to deny that the lower level scientific laws are obeyed by higher level aggregations of matter. As we have seen, DNA molecules obey the laws of chemistry and physics. It is just that these laws do not explain higher level concepts like information transfer or natural selection. It is important to note, in denying the reducibility of the brain's functions to chemistry and physics, what is *not* being said about the brain and the human qualities. There is no extra ingredient added to the complex organization of cells when it evolves to become a human brain (just as nothing extra is added when an embryo develops a brain) and thinks, loves and has aesthetic feelings.

Going back to the thermodynamics example, no extra ingredient is added to a box of gas molecules to give them an 'arrow of time' which molecules treated in isolation did not possess. The addition of an extra ingredient to make life, especially human life, is almost universally rejected by modern biologists — it is an error known traditionally as 'vitalism'. No, it is the aggregation of many parts into a complex whole which brings about these human characteristics. And, Christians would add, it was the emergence of reasoning beings with a moral awareness which was the purpose behind these components and their aggregation.

The subject of the human brain is so important that I have devoted a whole chapter to it, so further discussion is delayed until Chapter 7.

The appellation *downward causation* has been applied by Donald

Campbell to the realization that higher levels of organization, and scientific laws formulated at these higher levels, affect lower level entities. Campbell cites as an example the jaws of soldier termites. These are so enormous that the soldier cannot feed himself and has to be fed by worker termites. The protein out of which the jaw is formed is of course determined by the DNA which codes for it. However, it is also true that the DNA is determined by the efficacy of the jaws produced, together with the way they function socially in the termite community, through natural selection.[18] There is thus a complex two-way causal connection between levels in the scientific hierarchy.

Such a complex web of inter-level explanations is also evident in an example of Barnett's[19] (though he does not use the term downward causation). He cites populations in which a large percentage of members are deficient in a particular enzyme. The enzyme deficiency causes jaundice and premature death but it also protects against malaria, which is endemic in those regions where the deficiency occurs. Now the protection offered against malaria is an explanation at the level of ecology, the relationship of individuals and populations to their environments. The difference between normal and jaundiced individuals is explained in genetic and biochemical terms. Barnett makes the point that explanations are thus required at levels ranging from the physical to the ecological; we can also see that these different-level explanations interact — the environment leads to selection of certain genes, which in their turn enhance survival against malaria but also produce jaundice.

Ontological reductionism

All creatures are words of God.

(Meister Eckhart.)

Ontological reductionism is the name given to the idea that the scientific explanation of any phenomenon is the only valid one.

Thus if we can explain anything, be it the origin of life, or human consciousness or whatever, scientifically, then we have explained it, full stop. There is nothing more to be said. This is the real nub of 'nothing-buttery' and was what Donald MacKay had in mind when he originally coined that expression. It is closely related to epistemological reductionism, since often it is expressed in extreme reductionist language — we are 'nothing but atoms and molecules'. In ultra-simplistic terms, the whole is 'nothing but the sum of its parts'.

We note in passing that F. J. Ayala uses the term ontological reductionism in a slightly different sense from the above, namely to mean that 'the laws of physics and chemistry fully apply to all biological processes at the level of atoms and molecules'.[20] This is in opposition to vitalism which claims that something else must be added to inorganic material to give rise to living processes — be this 'vital force', 'entelechy', '*élan vital*', 'soul' or whatever. We have already seen that we can agree that the atoms and molecules of biological entities obey the laws of physics just as those of non-biological entities do; that truly biological processes emerge with greater aggregation and complexity; and that there is consequently no need to add any ingredient to physical entities to produce the biological (we shall have more to say about the Christian idea of the soul in Chapter 7). We thus stick to our original definition of ontological reductionism as true 'nothing-buttery'.

To illustrate ontological reductionism in this sense, MacKay gives the example of an electrical advertising sign.[21] This can be explained scientifically in terms of electric currents passing along a complex of wires to incandesce the filaments of a pattern of lamps. But this is of course to miss the whole point, which is the message being transmitted, in letters and words, of the advertisement. It is like seeing Hamlet merely as patterns of ink spots on the paper on which the play is written, or explaining the motions of all the electrons in the cathode ray tube of my TV but failing to see that I am watching tennis from Wimbledon.

There is a sort of blindness here which particularly afflicts scientists who use methodological reductionism as a tool. For example, there is a tendency to say that the workings of the human brain are fully explained in terms of synaptic firings brought about by electrochemical processes. In this way concepts like free will, intention, beauty, love and reason lose their meaning. We have already seen that, epistemologically, this explanation may not even be attainable (and we shall delve deeper into this in Chapter 7), but even if it were and one could carry the whole process down to the behaviour of the fundamental particles of physics, there would be no reason to deny the parallel, or complementary, explanation in higher level terms.

In the case of *Hamlet*, and the advertising sign, there are two parallel, complementary explanations which both apply. Both are valid, neither negates the other. Also the physical explanation is necessary to carry the true meaning — there would be no *Hamlet* without ink patterns or advertising sign without electrons moving. At the same time we do not need the language of advertising to study the motion of electrons, though we shall miss the true meaning if we confine ourselves to the latter.

I hope the reader can begin to see that there might be a hidden meaning, even a religious meaning, in physical phenomena. God can create the universe using physical laws and processes, with the end product human beings. The minds and emotions of these creatures can have meaning in their own right, although every atom of the human body obeys the laws of physics. God can speak to us through nature and our fellow creatures. Indeed the whole natural world might be regarded as a gigantic advertising sign for its creator — as the *Sanctus* in the Holy Communion service puts it, 'Heaven and earth are full of thy glory: Glory be to thee, O Lord most High.'

Of course it is not sufficient to postulate that there might be some parallel, complementary explanation to our existence and attributes; we need to examine some evidence for this and this we do in later chapters of this book. Meanwhile, let us note that the alternative, ontological reductionism, is ultimately self-destructive. This is because it denies purpose and meaning. As Professor J. B. S. Haldane observed, 'If my mental processes are determined wholly by the motions of atoms in my brain, I have no reason to suppose that my beliefs are true ... and hence I have no reason for supposing my brain to be composed of atoms'.[22] It is our brains that have taught us ontological reductionism, and, if ontological reductionism be true, then our brains are not to be trusted.

Reason cannot arise from the irrational. If I make the jump from the statements A = B and B = C to the statement A = C simply because certain synapses fire in the cerebral cortex of my brain then I have no grounds for believing my deduction: I am not apprehending truth but following some causal chain of actions linked back in the evolutionary tree to random motions of atoms. As C. S. Lewis cogently argues,[23] the operation of my reason is only valid if there exists an antecedent Reason not preceded by irrationality. This antecedent Reason Christians call God.

The popularizers revisited

We are survival machines — robot vehicles blindly programmed to preserve the selfish molecules known as genes. This is a truth which still fills me with astonishment.

(Richard Dawkins.[24])

I have taken Richard Dawkins as a representative in the biological sphere of a certain reductionist position, and Stephen Hawking as a physicist and cosmologist of another. I should like now to examine the views of these two scientists in the light of the foregoing discussion.

All that we have learnt in this chapter is in complete contradiction to the position of Dawkins who insists that biology is reducible to physics. Thus he says:

The body is a complex thing with many constituent parts, and to understand its behaviour you must apply the laws of physics to its parts, not to the whole. The behaviour of the whole will then emerge as a consequence of interactions of the parts.[25]

And again:

> My task is to explain elephants, and the world of complex things, in terms of the simple things that physicists either understand, or are working on.[26]

No, to repeat, time and again in practice we find that the emergent phenomena arising from complex wholes cannot solely be described in terms of, and could not be predicted from, the behaviour and physical laws governing the parts.

Dawkins completely fails to recognise downward causation. Thus:

> Living organisms exist for the benefit of DNA rather than the other way round.[27]

We have seen that DNA both determines phenotypic features (eg termite jaws) and is determined by them: it is a two way process.

Dawkins is also an ontological reductionist, for his repeated insistence that evolution explains why we are here and that we do not need to invoke a designer to understand life, or anything else in the universe, has the implication that there is nothing else to be said in explanation apart from the purely physical. He has no concept of a complementary explanation.

Somewhat in contrast to Dawkins, Steve Jones, Professor of Genetics at University College, London, who gave the highly acclaimed 1991 Reith Lectures, recognises the limitations of his field. In particular what makes a person cannot be reduced to his genetic constitution, and questions of meaning and purpose are beyond the realms of science. He says:

> It is the essence of all scientific theories that they cannot resolve everything. Science cannot answer the questions that philosophers — or children — ask: why are we here, what is the point of being alive, how ought we to behave? Genetics has almost nothing to say about what makes us more than just machines driven by biology, about what makes us human. These questions may be interesting, but scientists are no more qualified to comment on them than is anyone else. In its early days, human genetics suffered greatly from its

high opinion of itself. It failed to understand its own limits. Knowledge has brought humility to genetics as to other sciences; but the new awareness which genetics brings will also raise social and ethical problems which have as yet scarcely been addressed.[28]

It would appear that Stephen Hawking is also both an epistemological and an ontological reductionist. It is implicit that a physical Theory of Everything (TOE) will explain the whole of chemistry, biology and higher level sciences. At the end of *A Brief History of Time* he too sees the question why being answered by a physical theory alone. When we have a TOE, he says,

Then we shall all, philosophers, scientists, and just ordinary people, be able to take part in the discussion of why it is that we and the universe exist. If we find the answer to that, it would be the ultimate triumph of human reason — for then we would know the mind of God.[29]

No, we do not need a TOE to discuss these things and ultimate answers of this kind lie outside the realms of physics in what I have called complementary explanations. Interestingly, Bryan Appleyard sees them in human language, undoubtedly of prime importance, and notes that Wittgenstein's analysis of language was dismissed by Hawking a sentence or two before the passage I have just quoted. We shall return to the topic of language later; my own 'complementary' explanation is unashamedly the Christian one that God is working in and through nature. And God had more in his mind than fundamental physics in creating the world — rather he was expressing his own nature of love and faithfulness. But for the time being we stay with physics and mathematics, for there is much to learn about precisely to what the reductionists are aiming to reduce all science, which further undermines their case.

CHAPTER 6

De Revolutionibus:
The Twentieth Century

When to the new eyes of thee
All things by immortal power,
Near or far,
Hiddenly
To each other linked are,
That thou canst not stir a flower
Without troubling of a star.

(Francis Thompson, *The Mistress of Vision.*)

Let us summarize what we have learnt from the preceding chapter. Methodological reductionism is a basic component of scientific method; epistemological reductionism is at best only partially successful and severely deficient in reducing biology and the higher level sciences to physics; and ontological reductionism is an unfounded and ultimately self-destructive metaphysical belief.

We shall find in the present chapter that the reductionist programme is even further undermined in that it takes no account of the developments in mathematics and physics to which it attempts to reduce the rest of science. Both subjects have been through dramatic and revolutionary change in the present century, and these changes have deep implications. Not only do they revolutionize our view of the world, including the very nature of reality, but they impact in a fundamental way on epistemology, for they reveal clear and unbreachable limits to the knowledge which can be obtained by the methods of science. We begin with a look at the shaking of the very foundations of mathematics itself.

The crisis in mathematics

Mathematics is the door and the key to the sciences.

(Roger Bacon.[1])

Mathematics is the tool of science and, as Plato recognised, the foundation-stone of philosophy, taking pride of place in the 'national curriculum' of his Republic. Indeed, it has been said that the more mathematical a science becomes the more truly 'scientific' it is. The supreme example is physics, especially those modern esoteric branches of relativity and quantum theory. Chemistry is less mathematical and biology in its turn less again. However, recently even biology has become more mathematical, for example with the theory of games being applied to biological evolution. In this theory optimal strategies for animals (eg should an animal fight hard for territory with consequent risk or merely threaten?) can be worked out mathematically, and those animals with the best strategies will survive preferentially over the rest. Richard Dawkins has described this, quoting the work of Maynard Smith and others.[2]

What then is the logical and philosophical status of mathematics?

It may come as a surprise to many readers that the foundations of mathematics are somewhat precarious. Many people have the image of mathematics as exact, giving answers which can be checked and agreed upon. They would be surprised to read the verdict of Bertrand Russell, whose seminal work earlier this century (*Principia Mathematica*, with A N Whitehead) we discuss below: 'Mathematics may be defined as the subject in which we never know what we are talking about, nor whether what we are saying is true'. Yet at the heart of mathematics is a fundamental problem.

Any branch of mathematics, mathematical structure or system is founded upon axioms. The axioms are the premises which are taken to be self-evident for the system under discussion, though mathematics does not confine itself to systems which necessarily bear any relationship to the 'real world'. Indeed some pure mathematicians regard it as entirely fortuitous that their scribblings can be applied to reality, eg physics. Familiar examples of mathematical systems are arithmetic and Euclidean geometry.

Given the set-up of a mathematical system, and logical proce-dures for making deductions from the axioms, one would imagine that it would be possible to decide the truth or falsehood of any statement made within that system. If there is a logical sequence of deductions from the axioms which leads to the statement in ques-tion, it is proved. On the other hand a single counter-example would falsify the statement. For example, Pythagoras's theorem can be proved from the properties of congruent triangles, and the state-ment 'All odd numbers are prime' is falsified by the counter-exam-ple 9, which is divisible by 3.

What is very surprising is that, in any mathematical system at least as complex as arithmetic, there exist statements which we know to be true, yet which cannot be proved. To put it another way, you cannot have a consistent mathematical system which is also com-plete. This remarkable fact was discovered by the eminent Austrian mathematician Kurt Gödel and is known as Gödel's theorem. Basi-cally Gödel came up with the mathematical equivalent of the self-referential English language assertion, 'This statement is unprovable.' The statement was unprovable but therefore true. Roger Penrose goes through a simplified proof, accessible to the layman, of Gödel's theorem in *The Emperor's New Mind*.[3] Its significance for the human mind will be dealt with in Chapter 7. For a précis of Penrose's proof the reader is referred to my appendix.

The undecidability of mathematical statements within the logi-cal framework of the systems in which these statements are embed-ded is of fundamental importance to mathematics, and therefore to philosophy and science which are founded on mathematics. In the words of Douglas Hofstadter: 'Gödel showed that provability is a weaker notion than truth whatever axiomatic system is in-volved'.[4] It is sobering to recognise, from the proud edifice of math-ematics itself, that there are truths which cannot be proved. The consequences of this for physics will be explored below, but before doing so it is worth delving a little deeper into this matter. The non-mathematically minded are advised to skip over the details and just try and gather the gist of the argument. For the benefit of those who are not totally intimidated by equations, I have in any case relegated technical detail to the appendix!

Gödel published his famous theorem in 1931. It is worth stepping back a little to see what led up to this.

The foundations of mathematics were laid with the set theory of German mathematician Georg Cantor in the 1880s. A set is basically any collection of objects — one might speak of the set of black sheep or the set of odd numbers for example. By considering mappings between sets Cantor came up with some surprising results about infinity. Thus, in a very well defined sense there are the same (infinite!) 'number' of fractions as there are whole numbers, but more real numbers (numbers which can be expanded to infinitely many decimal places) than fractions. This is deeply counter-intuitive since there are infinitely many fractions between each pair of whole numbers, yet there is a one-to-one mapping between wholes and fractions. However, in the case of the reals and the fractions, where it is true that there are both infinitely many reals between any pair of fractions and infinitely many fractions between any pair of reals, no such mapping exists. Cantor showed that in the latter case, if we assume that such a mapping exists, we can always construct a real number with no fractional counterpart. The arithmetic devised by Cantor for dealing with the varying degrees of infinity is known as 'transfinite arithmetic'.

For the proof of Cantor's assertion that there are more reals than fractions the reader is referred to the appendix.

Nothing about these various degrees of infinity is truly illogical or paradoxical. However, a number of paradoxes in Cantor's set theory were soon forthcoming, and a body blow was dealt by Bertrand Russell, the celebrated British mathematician and philosopher. Some sets are members of themselves, others are not. For example the set of all sets is a member of itself, and so is the set of all non-black objects. However, the set of all black objects is not a member of itself. Russell posed the question, 'Is the set of all sets which are not members of themselves a member of itself?' The reader might need to spend a minute or two thinking about this, but basically the answer 'yes' and the answer 'no' both lead to contradictions. If this set is a member of itself then it ceases to be the set of all sets which are not members of themselves. On the other hand if it is not a member of itself then it is not the set of all sets which are not members of themselves. Penrose[5] gives the analogous case of a library with two catalogues. The first catalogue lists all books which refer to themselves, the second all books which do not refer to themselves. Into which catalogue should the second catalogue be entered?

Russell and his Cambridge colleague Alfred North Whitehead set about producing a revised version of set theory with such paradoxes eliminated. The result was their famous seminal work on the foundations of mathematics, called *Principia Mathematica* (the title echoing that of Newton's famous treatise), which got round the problem by only allowing a strictly hierarchical system of set membership. Thus basic objects belonged to first level sets, objects plus first level sets to second level sets and so on: an nth level set could only contain as members lower level sets and objects.

Russell and Whitehead's scheme was severely limiting in terms of what could be discussed as sets. Nevertheless, it was certainly hoped that they had achieved their aim of eliminating paradoxes. German mathematician David Hilbert issued a challenge to the mathematical world, namely to demonstrate rigorously that Russell and Whitehead's system was both consistent and complete. By consistent he meant that there were no contradictions within the system, and by complete that any statement of number theory could be proved within the system.

Hilbert's programme was smashed to pieces by Gödel's revolutionary paper. Not only did Gödel show that Russell and Whitehead's scheme contained unprovable but true statements, but much more generally that any mathematical system at least as complicated as arithmetic would do so. The reader is again referred to the appendix for a slightly more technical discussion and derivation of Gödel's theorem.

In a nutshell what Gödel did was to assign a number to each statement of arithmetic. He also, and this was the really cunning part of his achievement, assigned a number to each sequence of 'proofs' or logical steps in arithmetic. He then used this set-up to devise an arithmetic statement which said of itself that it had no proof! This 'Gödel statement' must be true because, if it is not, it is inconsistent. The choice is stark: either we have an axiomatic system which is consistent but incomplete because it contains true statements which cannot be proved, or it is an inconsistent system containing self-contradictions.

There are many subtleties which have been completely ignored in the above presentation (and indeed in the mathematical appendix for those who have dared to grapple with that), but I hope you have got the gist of the argument. If you have, you may nevertheless be thinking that these self-referential Gödel-type statements are all very esoteric, but the real question is, 'Are there any genuine, important statements in mathematics which are undecidable?' To answer this I will consider one example by returning to the various degrees of infinity investigated by Cantor. You will remember that Cantor showed that there are more real numbers than rational (ie fractional) ones. We say that the rationals are countably infinite (because they can be put into one-to-one correspondence with the whole numbers), and the reals (also called the continuum) are uncountably infinite. Now it is fairly easy to construct sets which are more infinite yet than reals. This can be done by considering power sets: the power set of a set is the set of all subsets of that set, a subset rather naturally being defined as a set whose elements are chosen to be some of the elements of the set in question.

The question which Cantor posed, and with which mathematicians have been wrestling ever since, was, 'Is there any degree of infinity (cardinality in the jargon) which lies between countably infinite and the continuum?' That is to say, can we construct a set with more members than the fractions, but fewer than the reals, in the well-defined sense of transfinite arithmetic? Cantor did not believe that this was possible, but could not prove it; he labelled his belief the 'Continuum Hypothesis'.

Sadly, Cantor himself spent so much intellectual energy on this problem that it drove him mad. It was left first to Gödel, and more recently to American mathematician Paul Cohen, to shed light on it, with very surprising results.

What Gödel showed was that, if we simply add the continuum hypothesis to the axioms of set theory, it does not lead to any contradictions. Then in 1963 Cohen showed that if we add the converse of the continuum hypothesis to the axioms of set theory, we find that this also cannot lead to a contradiction! Thus the continuum hypothesis is completely independent of the axioms of set theory! It can therefore be neither proved nor disproved from those axioms.

Of course, that it can neither be proved nor disproved from the axioms does not tell us whether the continuum hypothesis is true. Gödel himself thought, for him surely rather oddly, that we had not got the axioms of set theory right and that if we added appropriate axioms we could demonstrate the continuum hypothesis one way or the other. But, as Barrow points out,[6] there would still be undecidable propositions in any new system we came up with. Barrow and Penrose give examples of recently discovered, ostensibly innocent, mathematical statements with the Gödel property.[7,8]

Alan Turing, the brilliant Cambridge mathematician whose seminal work on computing was so important in cracking the German Enigma codes during the second world war, came up with an equivalent to Gödel's theorem in computing. He was also responding to a challenge of Hilbert, namely to demonstrate whether there was a universal mechanical procedure for deriving all mathematical truths. Such procedures are called algorithms and are in essence just like the proofs in Gödel's scheme. Turing postulated a hypothetical computing machine, called a Turing machine, which in an idealized way captures all the essential features of modern computers. Basically, a Turing machine takes an input stream of numbers, carries out some processing on it, and outputs another stream. Different Turing machines carry out different operations, and so one devises a sequence of Turing machines which act on a given number m. Turing saw that Hilbert's challenge was equivalent to the question, 'Does a particular Turing machine stop, ie come to the end of its task, or go on for ever, never coming to a halt?'

We can see that the question is actually equivalent to whether certain mathematical theorems can be proved or not, as follows. Take as an example the statement known as Goldbach's conjecture that every even number greater than 2 can be written as the sum of two primes. A Turing machine could go through all particular cases, only stopping at an even number for which all partitions into a sum of two numbers involve non-primes. Turing demonstrated that there is no general algorithm for deciding whether the machines will stop (so, for example, we are still no wiser as regards Goldbach's conjecture!) His proof very much resembled Cantor's 'diagonal slash' proof that there are more real numbers than rationals given in the appendix.

Turing also examined the notion of 'computability'. It turns out that for some infinite decimals, like p, there exists an algorithm for calculating each digit in turn. Of course the whole number could not be produced in one go, since it has infinitely many digits. However, there is an algorithm for producing its digits one by one. In most cases, however, there is no such algorithm — most real numbers are non-computable. For example one could define a number whose nth digit is 1 if the nth Turing machine acting on n stops and 0 if it does not.

Gödel's theorem and the undecidability of propositions in arithmetic and higher mathematical systems have important implications for physics. For physics, as we have seen, is based on mathematics. Moreover, the mathematics utilized in physics is more complicated than arithmetic — it involves the real number system, not just the natural numbers. The entities which are the stuff of physics — space, time, fields, wave functions and so on — are defined using the real number system. The equations governing these quantities map real numbers as inputs for initial conditions and boundary conditions onto real numbers describing their evolution in space and time. It follows that physics is inevitably incomplete (we shall meet below 'computability' limits to it in discussing chaos theory, which relates to the accuracy to which we can specify real numbers).

Stephen Hawking's Theory of Everything will be no such thing: the search for a TOE is doomed to failure. In any case, might not a TOE be the ultimate self-referencing statement: could it explain itself?

The truly profound implications of Gödel's theorem for physics, and in particular for the prospect of finding a TOE, have of course not gone unnoticed by physicists and cosmologists. Let me quote from three of the most eminent, all professors. Russell Stannard rubs salt into the wounds by combining his comments on Gödel's theorem with the observation that the axioms of a mathematical system cannot be justified from within it:

> This inherent, unavoidable lack of completeness must reflect itself in whatever mathematical system models our universe. As creatures belonging to the physical world, we will be included as part of that model. It follows that we shall never be able to justify the choice of axioms in the model — and consequently the physical laws to which these axioms correspond. Nor shall we be able to account for all the true statements that can be made about the universe.[9]

And he concludes:

> For these reasons the goal of a complete theory of everything is unattainable, and the claim to have disproved the need for a Creator is false.[10]

I shall expand on this last point in Chapter 9. In the mean time, reference must be made to John Barrow's book *Theories of Everything*. Barrow makes the point that the devastating conclusions we have come to above would be vitiated if physical reality were ultimately expressible in some mathematical system simpler than arithmetic (eg Presburger arithmetic which has addition on the whole numbers and zero, but no subtraction).[11] However, perhaps in part reflecting the unreality of this prospect, towards the end of the book he too describes some far-reaching limitations to what a TOE will provide. He says that beauty, simplicity and truth cannot be captured by a finite collection of logical rules: 'No non-poetic account of reality will be complete.'[12] He goes on:

The scope of Theories of Everything is infinite but bounded; they are necessary parts of a full understanding of things but they are far from sufficient to unravel the subtleties of a universe like ours ... There is no formula that can deliver all truth, all harmony, all simplicity. No Theory of Everything can ever provide total insight. For, to see through everything, would leave us seeing nothing at all.[13]

My third commentator on Gödel and TOEs is Paul Davies, who concludes:

So the search for a genuinely unique Theory of Everything that would eliminate all contingency and demonstrate that the physical world must necessarily be as it is, seems to be doomed to failure on grounds of logical consistency. No rational system can be both consistent and complete. There will always remain some openness, some element of mystery, something unexplained.[14]

There are other lessons to be drawn from Gödel's theorem and the associated work of Turing. An important point to which we shall return in Chapter 7 is that it would appear that human minds can 'see' mathematical truths which have no proof in formal logical systems. The notion of truth is wider than any formal system of logic, to invert Hofstadter's statement. Conversely, there is a limit to what can be known by the application of deductive algorithmic procedures.

Computers operate by executing algorithms. There is thus a limit to the capability of computers which is exceeded by human minds, which clearly have the non-algorithmic capacity to apprehend mathematical truth.

Let us now turn to physics, which has also undergone the most profound revolution in our century.

Death of the clockwork universe

With Earth's first Clay They did the Last Man knead,
And there of the Last Harvest sow'd the Seed:
   And the first Morning of Creation wrote
What the last Dawn of Reckoning shall read.

(Edward Fitzgerald, *The Rubáiyát of Omar Khayyám*, ed. 1, liii, ed. 4, lxxiii.)

We have seen that until the advent of relativity and quantum theory Newton's laws of motion were the basis of physics. Let us for the moment ignore all that we have learnt about emergent properties and the difficulties with the reductionist programme from Chapter 5; we shall return to them shortly from within physics itself. Newton's laws govern the behaviour of elementary particles and, assuming then that everything in the universe is made of particles simply obeying these laws, an entirely deterministic universe follows.

It was Laplace in particular who made the leap from Newton's laws to universal determinism. He said:

> We may regard the present state of the Universe as the effect of its past and the cause of its future. An intellect which at any given moment knew all the forces that animate nature and the mutual positions of the beings that compose it, if this intellect were vast enough to submit its data to analysis, could condense into a single formula the vast movement of the greatest bodies of the universe and that of the lightest atom: for such an intellect nothing could be uncertain; and the future just like the past would be present before its eyes.[15]

As Barrow points out, however, Leibniz had made an even more explicit statement some hundred years previously:

> Now each cause has its specific effect which would be produced by it ... If, for example, one sphere meets another sphere in free space and if their sizes and their paths and directions before collision

were known, we can then foretell and calculate how they will re-bound and what course they will take after the impact ... From this one sees then that everything proceeds mathematically — that is, infallibly — in the whole wide world, so that if someone could have sufficient insight into the inner parts of things, and in addi-tion had remembrance enough to consider all the circumstances and to take them into account, he would be a prophet and would see the future in the present as in a mirror.[16]

This purely mechanistic view of the universe has had a pro-found impact on philosophy and indeed theology. If my brain is composed of particles governed by deterministic laws, how can I as an individual possess free will? And if I do not possess free will, how can I be responsible for my actions, for then I am purely an automaton? Even more importantly, where is there room for God to act in the world? Of course he is able to break the laws he has ordained if he is an omnipotent being. But this is a very unsatisfy-ing explanation of God's action, especially if it is the only way we can see him acting. For if he only intervenes on rare occasions, miraculously breaking his own laws as it were, why does he do so on some occasions and not others? These occasional interventions in the natural process would seem to be very arbitrary. Did God get the laws of nature wrong in the first place that such interventions are necessary? Also, there is a great deal of suffering in the world and it would be natural in the light of that to ask why there is not much more such intervention by God. On the other hand, we have seen already that the great success of the scientific endeavour has relied on there being order in the universe — the universe is not subject to whimsical, inexplicable behaviour but is subject to the laws of physics which man has discovered.

Newton himself failed to take the leap to total determinism, invoking God to push things along a little when the system got into trouble. This is the notorious 'God of the gaps' argument, rightly discredited because, if we keep finding physical explana-tions for the phenomena for which we are invoking God, where does that leave God?

So this traditional scientific, deterministic view of the universe is inimical both to the status of man as the free, rational creature he perceives himself to be, and to the actions of God in the world. We shall return specifically to the question of God's action in the world in Chapter 9. In the mean time, let us ask, 'Is this a true picture?'

We have already seen that in the modern scientific view of the universe Newton's laws have been overthrown and chance now plays a significant rôle in both physics and biology. Let us concentrate for the moment on quantum theory, which has revolutionized our understanding of the smallest constituents of matter. Heisenberg's Uncertainty Principle tells us that it is not possible simultaneously to measure with total precision (for example) both the position and the momentum of an electron. If we measure the one accurately, the other is infinitely imprecise. The very act of observation affects the result of that observation, so that observer and observed are inextricably interlinked.

Most physicists believe that this indeterminacy is a consequence of 'the way the world is' (it is *ontological* in the philosophers' jargon), and is not due to some fault or inaccuracy in our measuring instruments. There is indeed a quantity, the wave function, which evolves deterministically (according to Schrödinger's equation). However, this wave function only tells us the probability of a particular event occurring. Following an observation, the wave function 'collapses' to a particular value which provides the initial condition for the next evolution determined by Schrödinger's equation.

The picture that emerges is one in which successive events are determined according to chance, though with a definite probability, in total contrast to the deterministic picture discussed above in which each successive event is totally determined by those which have gone before. If we repeat an experiment with two possible outcomes many times, the result will come down one way a given proportion of the times according to the probability of the event, and the other way the rest of the time. In classical Newtonian theory it would come out the same way every time.

On the face of it quantum theory would seem to have destroyed determinism. And perhaps it has, at least from a philosophical point of view. However, there is a problem, because when you aggregate matter together to the macroscopic scale — the scale of every day objects — what happens is that all the quantum uncertainty is smoothed out and determinism rules again. The motion of all the atoms comprising a billiard ball is probabilistic, but when these motions are aggregated, the motion of the ball is determined by Newton's laws. Newton's laws are a very, very accurate approximation to the laws of quantum mechanics at the macroscopic scale, so accurate that all uncertainty is effectively removed.

Actually, the above is a slight over-simplification. Experiments can be devised in which quantum effects influence macroscopic ones directly. In Schrödinger's famous thought experiment a cat in a box is poisoned by the breaking of a phial triggered by the radio-active decay of an atom — a quantum event occurring probabilistically. The cat is in some hybrid dead/alive state until a human observer looks into the box to see! We shall ignore such contrived events in what follows.

Forgetting Schrödinger's cat, is determinism correct after all? Does man have free will or is he a robot, programmed to run according to the clockwork laws of Newtonian mechanics? My brain is composed of cells — macroscopic entities for which quantum uncertainty can be ignored — and therefore it obeys Newton's laws. We clearly need to take a more critical look at the Laplacian view we outlined earlier. To remind you, this states that if we know all the positions and velocities of all the particles in the universe at a given time, then we can, at least in principle, predict their future positions and velocities indefinitely far into the future.

The vital key to the question of predictability is the way in which errors in the initial measurements propagate in a system, that is, how such errors affect the future predictions. For some simple systems, for example a pendulum swinging in two dimensions or a single planet orbiting a star, Laplacian predictability is valid because errors propagate linearly. That is, as time goes on the errors in my prediction increase only slowly. If I double the time for which

I am predicting my error doubles, if I treble it the error is multiplied by three, and so on. To achieve the same accuracy at twice the time I would need to halve the errors in my original measurements, at three times the time I would need my original errors to be one third of what they were, etc.

The interesting point is, that for some systems which are only marginally more complicated than those quoted, for example a pendulum swinging in three dimensions or a dust particle in the gravitational field of two planets (Hill's reduced three body problem[17]) the motion is *chaotic*. In this case errors propagate exponentially. Every time step of a certain duration, the error will double, instead of increasing by the same amount. In a short space of time these errors will completely swamp my ability to predict. Correspondingly, to obtain the same accuracy farther ahead will mean having to reduce the initial errors to infinitesimal proportions. The behaviour of such a system will appear random, not regular as for the cases discussed above. A case in point is our inability to predict the weather more than a day or two in advance and the familiar claim that a butterfly's wings flapping in Australia today may cause a tornado in Texas tomorrow. Very tiny perturbations in initial conditions cause wide divergences in predicted results. Polkinghorne gives the example of molecules in a gas, which behave essentially like small billiard balls:

> After only 10^{-10} seconds, fifty or more collisions have taken place for each molecule. After even so few collisions the resulting outcome is so sensitive that it would be affected by the variation in the gravitational field due to an extra electron on the other side of the universe — the weakest force due to the smallest particle the furthest distance away ![18]

Polkinghorne's argument becomes even stronger if we take into account the fact that, because of the cosmic expansion, matter is continuously crossing the horizon into the visible universe from beyond it. For this new matter can have had no causal connection with the visible universe and therefore we cannot, even in principle, know what its effect might be.[19]

Ultimately the limiting factor in prediction is the real number system itself. To express any initial input precisely requires a decimal with an infinite number of places. Any cut-off to a finite number of decimal places constitutes an error which propagates so rapidly that prediction is impossible. And to provide infinitely many decimal places is clearly impossible for this requires infinite information, beyond the resources of computers and finite human beings alike. As we have seen, the digits of most real numbers are literally non-computable. And of course, remembering Gödel's theorem, even if we could give a complete description of the initial state of nature we could never be sure of its consistency. Further recalling the argument on ontological reductionism of Chapter 5, the Laplacian universe could never give rise to reason, and since it is through reason that we apprehend the Laplacian view, we have no grounds for believing it.

Does not all this show simply that the universe is intrinsically unpredictable? It is still theoretically deterministic — predictability and determinism are not the same thing. Newton's laws are deterministic even if we require infinitesimal accuracy in initial conditions to predict from them. I think the fact that there are influences we can in principle know nothing about (those beyond the observable universe's horizon) does lead to indeterminism, but also of course the requirement of infinitesimal accuracy does lead us back into the quantum realm with its inherent uncertainty. Quantum theory is intrinsically indeterminate and we now see that it impacts on the macroscopic through the requirement of infinitesimal accuracy of measurement, a fundamental barrier to knowledge because of Heisenberg's Uncertainty Principle.

To be truly certain that this last argument is correct, one needs to await research in the realm of quantum chaos, a study only yet in its infancy. In the mean time Polkinghorne questions whether we have it right in stipulating deterministic laws with unpredictable behaviour following from them.

'Which is the approximation and which is the reality?'[20] he asks. He suggests a form of downward causation in which the simple deterministic laws emerge at a lower level from high level behaviour which does not possess this property. Moreover, we have obtained the lower level laws by treating systems as if they were isolated from the whole, a procedure intrinsically impossible. The deterministic laws thus represent only an approximation to reality.

It must not be thought that the theory of chaos demolishes the idea of order in the universe, far from it. Indeed 'chaos' is something of a misnomer. Thus, although detailed prediction is impossible, what does happen in chaotic systems is that they tend to explore a limited range of behaviours, called 'strange attractors'. The key point is that no behaviour is precisely repeated, for then one would have infinitely repeating cycles, but rather the set of all possible behaviours is bounded. Strange attractors reveal order within the disorder of chaotic systems.[21]

The work of Ilya Prigogine and his collaborators at the University of Brussels reveals other interesting properties arising out of purely classical (non-quantum) physics, particularly how order arises out of disorder. Prigogine has studied dynamical systems far away from equilibrium which receive energy input from the environment. What he finds is spontaneous self-organization triggered by minute effects. For example, in the 'chemical clock' the concentrations of different chemicals oscillate back and forth between different values, seemingly involving the collaboration of billions of molecules. Prigogine and Stengers liken this to the molecules being coloured blue and red and simultaneously, at regular intervals, all changing their identity.[22] This is quite unexpected: purely chaotic behaviour of the molecules would lead one to expect a mixed 'violet' colour with occasional flashes of blue or red as these preponderate on a random basis. Instead, we have all blue followed by all red. Their work, involving spontaneous self-organization arising out of disorder, very importantly against a background of the second law of thermodynamics which speaks of irreversibility and overall increasing disorder in the universe, has led Prigogine and Stengers to speak of the 're-enchantment of nature'.[23]

As Polkinghorne points out[24] the physical systems in question here are far less complex than the simplest living cell, yet exhibit such surprising, emergent behaviour.

We have seen in the above a trend towards a more holistic physics. In particular we have seen the impossibility of isolating the phenomena we wish to study from the rest of the universe. There are two further aspects of this unity of the universe which it is worth looking at.

In Chapter 3, we mentioned the famous Einstein-Podolsky-Rosen (EPR) thought experiment in quantum mechanics. Suppose, for example, that an electrically neutral particle with spin zero decays into an electron and a positron, each spin ½ particles. Since spin is conserved in this process, if we measure the spin of the electron in some direction, then the spin of the positron must automatically be in the opposite direction. These particles might now be light-years apart, even at opposite ends of the universe. Measurement on the one seems to communicate its effect to the other faster than the speed of light (in fact, instantaneously), in violation of relativity.

Everything would be alright for this experiment on a classical picture since the spin states would then be fixed at the decay time. The problem arises because in quantum theory it is the act of measurement which fixes the spin of the electron (it is indeterminate until measured): hence the instantaneous transmission of the opposite value to the positron and hence the paradox.

In fact experiments by French physicist Alain Aspect seem to confirm the reality of the EPR paradox — these effects do in essence travel faster than light. Quantum theory thus exhibits non-local effects; there is an inter-relatedness between different parts of the universe of a most fundamental kind. Isolation of the phenomena under discussion, as traditionally done in science, is intrinsically impossible, and a new holism reigns.

This holism is apparent on the large scale in physics too. Newton's laws of motion, which we described in Chapter 3, apply only in a restricted set of reference frames, called inertial frames, which are moving uniformly with respect to each other. The earth itself is not such a frame. In order to make Newton's laws work, fictitious (so-called 'inertial') forces must be introduced. For the rotating earth these are known as centrifugal and Coriolis forces. What we are really searching for in physics, however, are universal laws which apply in all frames. So the question arises, 'To what can we attribute these seemingly fictitious forces?' Bishop Berkeley and later Ernst Mach concluded that they must be attributed to the earth's rotation relative to the 'fixed stars', that is in practice to the average motion of all the matter in the universe. The inertial frames are simply those which are not accelerated (acceleration includes rotation) relative to the fixed stars. Physical effects from the distant stars come into play when matter is accelerated relative to them.[25] This idea is now known as Mach's Principle.

It was Einstein, with his general theory of relativity, who produced the beautifully consistent picture which unifies gravitational and inertial forces and describes how matter produces a curved space-time geometry. Although the detailed relationship of general relativity to Mach's Principle is a complex, and to a certain extent still open, question, here too we are seeing a holism embracing all parts of the universe.

Where has this excursion into modern theories of quantum mechanics, chaos, non-equilibrium systems and general relativity led us? We have seen that we do not live in a clockwork universe. In the words of Polkinghorne there is an intrinsic openness in the behaviour of dynamical systems. As he says:

> There is an emergent property of flexible process, even within the world of classical physics, which encourages us to see Newton's rigidly deterministic account as no more than an approximation to a more supple reality.[26]

Besides seeing the phenomenon of emergence arising within physics itself, we have also seen that a new holism is evident in the great revolutionary theories of physics, general relativity and quantum theory. It is no longer adequate or even possible to isolate phenomena from their surroundings, or indeed from the universe at large. The EPR experiment shows that quantum theory, the theory of the very small, is fundamentally non-local, and Mach's Principle shows the same for the large-scale.

We consider in Chapter 9 how the picture of the universe presented by modern physics is compatible with the Christian view of God's acting in the world.

CHAPTER 7

What is a Human ?

What a piece of work is a man! How noble in reason! how infinite in faculty! in form and moving, how express and admirable! in action, how like an angel! in apprehension, how like a god! the beauty of the world! the paragon of animals! And yet, to me, what is this quintessence of dust?

(*Hamlet*, Act II, scene ii, line 316.)

In Chapter 5 we examined the various forms of scientific reductionism in some detail, but because of its importance we postponed consideration of what it ultimately means to be human to a separate chapter. Of course a single chapter is inadequate to do justice to this vast topic, on which many volumes have been written. My limited intention is to point to three key areas where reductionist statements have been made and where they fail.

These areas are: the relationship of the mind to the brain, where it is asserted that consciousness either does not really exist or is of no importance; modern evolutionary biology where the idea is put about that man is simply a 'gene survival machine'; and modern computer science, particularly the discipline of artificial intelligence, where the idea that he is a computer is in vogue.

The classical mind-body problem

'The dogma of the Ghost in the Machine' ... is entirely false, and false not in detail but in principle.

(Gilbert Ryle.[1])

"I believe in the ghost in the machine".

(Sir Karl Popper.[2])

The figure of one man looks down across three and a half centuries to dominate all discussion of the relationship between mind and body: that man is the great French philosopher and mathematician René Descartes.

In answer to the supreme epistemological question 'What can I know?' Descartes came up with his famous dictum *Cogito ergo sum*, in English 'I think, therefore I am'. Having pared away all things doubtful and uncertain the one paramount reality is my own existence or selfhood, and this *because I think*. This led Descartes on to his famous separation of subjects, which fundamentally are conscious thought, and material objects — the notion of Cartesian dualism. He argued that the guarantee of the existence of the material world can come only from God, who is perfect and trustworthy — he does not deceive us. This division into subject and object, observer and observed, has been fundamental to scientific method (although we have begun to see its breakdown in modern physics, especially quantum theory).

Descartes separated mind from body, but failed to account satisfactorily for their interaction — in particular how can non-material consciousness influence the material world? I am not convinced that we have yet answered this question today but a number of reductionist attempts have been made which I shall now describe.

One approach to mind-body interaction is to ignore the problem altogether. For example, in B. F. Skinner's behaviourism (as described in his book *Beyond Freedom and Dignity*[3]) all that matters is stimulus and response. The brain is treated as a black box and, although conscious experience is not specifically denied, it plays a meaningless rôle. Human behaviour will be completely explained by investigations of the pattern of stimulus and response, and indeed when we have this explanation human behaviour will be entirely controllable by so-called 'operant conditioning'. As Nobel prizewinning neurophysiologist Sir John Eccles remarks,[4] this leads to a caricature of man, for it ignores what for him is the prime reality, namely his personal, conscious experience. I would also suggest that this approach is non-scientific in the sense that there is clearly an area of investigation here, of signal importance, which behaviourism encourages us to ignore.

Other approaches recognise that it is important to study the brain, but still deny any meaningful rôle to the mind. Thus the view known as 'epiphenomenalism' accedes that the mind exists but insists that it exerts no causal influence. Conscious experiences are merely a froth on the surface of brain processes. This view was propounded by Thomas Huxley, the great Darwinian, yet, as Popper points out,[5] it is in fundamental conflict with Darwinism. This is because Darwinism suggests we look for survival value in any evolved feature and if epiphenomenalism were true there could be none in having a mind.

A subtle variant of this is the psychoneural identity hypothesis of Herbert Feigl.[6] This says that conscious experiences really exist but are identical to brain states. The two are really different ways of seeing the same thing, namely the internal (consciousness) and the external (the brain). Thus there can be a causal interaction from mind to brain because they are the same thing! This gives a stronger rôle to the mind, though it may be argued only through a semantic conjuring trick. Since explanations in terms of mind are essentially redundant in this picture, because they can be achieved in terms of the corresponding physical processes, Darwinism is still violated.

It is curious that, perhaps contrary to expectation, we can invoke Darwinism in refutation of certain reductionist views of the human mind. However, it is important to ask, notwithstanding any conflict with Darwinism, are these views that mind events are somehow identical with, or mere epiphenomena of, brain events supported by that branch of science which deals specifically with the brain? Sir John Eccles makes the point that such views are naïve with regard to brain states, which 'have a patterned operation in space and time of an almost infinite complexity, with only a minute fraction — less than 1 per cent of cortical activity — ever giving the subject a conscious experience'.[7]

The quite remarkable split brain experiments carried out over a number of years by Roger Sperry and his associates are extremely interesting for their insights into brain functioning and its relationship to conscious experience. Eccles discusses them, as does mathematician Roger Penrose.[8] The human brain comprises two hemispheres, the left (dominant in 98% of us) and right (minor), which communicate via the great cerebral commisure (the *corpus callosum*). The dominant hemisphere is so-called because the linguistic areas are located there. However, although the two hemispheres look almost symmetrical, there are very distinct functions and abilities associated with them. For example, arithmetic and computational skills are associated with the dominant hemisphere and musical and spatio-temporal skills with the minor hemisphere.

Subjects of split-brain experiments are patients who have undergone surgical commisurotomy for therapeutic reasons (severe and uncontrollable epilepsy): thus the two hemispheres of their brains no longer communicate. It is important to note that the corpus callosum contains some 200 million nerve bundles, so traffic between these hemispheres in normal circumstances is quite prodigious.

Events in the left visual field are processed by the right brain hemisphere. In the commisurotomy patients they give rise to no conscious experience communicated by the speaking subject. The patients can, however, respond to left field stimuli, eg in picking up coins in their left hands when dollar signs are flashed at the left (no mean feat — they are not actually shown coins). They report all such movement as unconscious, involuntary and uncontrolled. When asked about it a subject will respond with words to the effect that he cannot feel anything in the left hand and did not voluntarily use it.

Thus we are led to liken the right hemisphere to a sophisticated animal brain, but giving rise to no measurable conscious experience. This was Eccles's conclusion in 1977:

> Despite all this apparently intelligent behaviour, the subject never derives any conscious experience from the goings-on in the minor hemisphere in all of its operative procedures.[9]

Later experiments have served to modify this rather categorical assertion, and it now appears that the right hemisphere does indeed have some conscious experience. Of course this is difficult to detect since the speech centres are in the dominant hemisphere, and so communication by the right hemisphere is comparatively rudimentary.

On being provided with pictorial representations, say of a cat and dog, and signs spelling the words 'cat' and 'dog', in the left visual field, the right hemisphere is able to associate the words with the objects. Thus far there is therefore some linguistic ability. However, the right brain is unable to complete even the simplest sentences. The subject's right brain is also able to recognise pictures of persons, including himself, and familiar objects and scenes. Specification of these things was, however, difficult and could only be obtained by 'highly informative prompting'.[10] Nevertheless these experiments do seem to show some limited self-consciousness for the right hemisphere. Eccles remains unconvinced that they are enough to confer personhood on the right brain alone — for this one would need to have evidence of planning for the future, and decision making based on some value system. It is difficult to see how these qualities could be present, as they are for the fully self-conscious left brain, without language.

In fact the importance of language in the development of a human person with cognitive and creative abilities has also been studied scientifically, notably the case cited by Eccles of a 13½ year old girl isolated from birth from all human contact. The usual speech areas in the left brain had atrophied and the right brain took over, but with severe problems — after 2 years only three or four words could be strung together to form a sentence. However there was substantial linguistic and cognitive progress. The case of Helen Keller is also instructive: she was blind, deaf and dumb, and exhibited extreme behavioural problems until she had been taught to communicate through language via the medium of touch.

Popper believes that moral concepts are dependent on language. While animals may have a degree of consciousness 'only a man can make an effort to become a better man; to master his fears, his laziness, his selfishness; to get over his lack of self-control'.[11] And it is language which is the key to this self-critical capacity. Wittgenstein is of course the modern philosopher who pointed to language as being essentially social and of prime importance in conferring selfhood on humans. Without language, thinking is impossible.

Wilder Penfield, the eminent Canadian neurosurgeon responsible for much of the mapping of the various sensory and motor areas of the brain in the 1940s and 1950s, has artificially stimulated various areas of the brain. This can be done to patients undergoing brain surgery because the brain itself does not have pain receptors; hence only local anaesthetic is necessary and patients are fully conscious. It is especially interesting that electrical stimulation of the motor cortex of conscious subjects undergoing brain surgery gives rise to actions disowned by the subject. A subject describes such an action as done to him, not by him. There is clearly therefore some difference in the way motor actions are processed as a result of will from when they are artificially stimulated. As noted by MacKay, however, some stimulations (such as thirst and visual experiences) are accepted by the patient, so the overall position is quite complex.[12]

S. A. Barnett makes the obvious but important point that, when the brain is exposed, one sees just a jelly-like mass: 'one does not see thoughts'. He goes on to say:

> Whatever is done to it, one cannot, by observing only the brain itself, reveal a personality with feelings, intentions and memories. Penfield's observations were a result, not of recording nerve impulses or the EEG, but of asking the patient questions, and of listening to the answers.[13]

From the scientific evidence, Sir John Eccles is particularly scathing about the denial of the interaction between mind and brain of the psychoneural identity hypothesis and other 'parallelist' variants. Such theories lead to the idea that to will an action is an illusion. If this is true it is self-defeating — this idea itself is illusory:

I have learned the futility of arguing about whether one has free will or not. The plain fact is that each of us experiences it and any attempt at denial can claim no more authority than a reflex built by operant conditioning. I do not argue with purely reflexing systems![14]

Sir Karl Popper has made a similar point: determinism if true cannot be argued, since any such argument is presumably itself determined by purely physical conditions, as are any opposing arguments ...[15]

Eccles concludes from the split-brain and electrical stimulation experiments that psychoneural parallelism has been falsified. The minor hemisphere is highly sophisticated, with ability in complex pattern recognition, spatial relations, and even in intelligent and learned activities; it is also almost symmetrical to the dominant hemisphere. Yet it gives rise to only limited conscious experience. This is not what one would expect from psychoneural identity and its variants, at least in the straightforward form that there is a one-to-one mapping from all brain states to conscious experiences. I think this conclusion is still valid despite the fact that now there is some evidence of conscious experience in the right brain rather than none, which was Eccles's assumption when he first made this point.

Eccles favours rather a form of dualistic interactionism in which the conscious self interacts causally (in both directions) with a particular part of the dominant hemisphere he calls the liaison brain. This is in accord with the interpretation of Sperry himself of his split-brain experiments:

Conscious phenomena in this scheme are conceived to interact with and to largely govern the physiochemical and physiological aspects of the brain process. It obviously works the other way round as well, and thus a mutual interaction is conceived between the physiological and the mental properties. Even so, the present interpretation would tend to restore mind to its old prestigious position over matter, in the sense that the mental phenomena are seen to transcend the phenomena of physiology and biochemistry.

Consciousness does do things and is highly functional as an important component of the causal sequence in higher level reactions. This is a view that puts consciousness to work. It gives the phenomena of consciousness a use and a reason for being and for having been evolved.[16]

Thus the scientific evidence is against identity of mind events and brain events and would seem to favour a form of dualistic interaction. This view is supported by a more philosophical look at the problem. It is easy to see that there might be a correlation between certain mind events and brain events, for example the sensation of pain in my leg might well be associated with very particular neurophysiological processes, and these might be the same from individual to individual. However for more abstract mental states it is very hard to see how there can possibly be such a one-to-one correspondence between the mental and the physical. For example, the state of seeing that something is money could be associated with an infinite variety of neurophysiological events. For, to start with, money can take a variety of physical forms each associated with different visual responses in the brain. It would be strange indeed if these distinct visual stimuli all produced the same neurophysiological effects on the brain. The difference between pain and money is the dependence of the latter on a conceptual framework expressed in language. It is what makes the distinction between us and animals. Philosopher John Searle concludes from this that a true science of the mental is impossible. However, for animals who may have some consciousness but lack the 'self-referentiality that goes with having human languages and social institutions' such a science may well be possible.[17]

Even if a close correlation between brain states and mind states could be established, to the extent that an external observer by examining a brain could tell precisely what thoughts were going on in the mind of the subject, it would be fallacious to conclude that mind and brain were identical. Donald MacKay, in an argument reminiscent of his critique of ontological reductionism, gives the analogy of a computer executing a program, say to solve a quadratic equation.[18] By examining the hardware and the processing going on in it one could, with ingenuity, deduce the correlation between machine states and steps in the solution of the equation. But it would be absurd to say that any machine states were the same as, say, the coefficients or the roots of the equation. Just as the message of an advertising sign is not to be identified with the wiring pattern of the lamps used to display it, so an equation is not the same as the electronic hardware used to solve it, and so also is the human mind not the same as the brain.

MacKay's own view is in fact a form of 'dual action' rather than dualism. He believes indeed that 'every aspect of our conscious experience has a *correlate* in some aspect of our brain activity',[19] although such correlates may be complex and not one-to-one. He distinguishes between the 'I-story' of conscious experience — I hear, I believe, and so on — and the corresponding brain events. He says:

> ... my mental activity and the correlated activity of my brain need not be thought of as two trains of parallel events, but rather as 'inner' and 'outer' aspects of the one complex (and mysterious) train of events that constitute my conscious agency. On this view the I-story' and the brain story are logically complementary, each bearing witness to essential facts which the other may systematically ignore.[20]

In his 1986 Gifford Lectures Mackay expressed his view that we do not have to think of 'the two as parallel streams of events, maintained in synchronism in some way'. Rather, 'our conscious experience is embodied in our brain activity: neither on the one hand identical with it, nor on the other hand quasi-physically interactive with it.'[21]

MacKay's view is supported by Christian psychologists David Myers and Malcolm Jeeves who also see a progressive tightening of the links between mind and brain. They see talking about the brain and talking about the mind as two levels of description much as MacKay's advertising sign can be described in terms of lamps or the message conveyed.[22]

Now when we engage in conscious activity, something is undoubtedly going on in the brain, and some success has been achieved in discovering the 'correlates', for example in recognition of faces. And while such research must continue, I remain somewhat sceptical, because of the arguments advanced earlier, that anything like a complete correlation can be achieved. I am also not persuaded that an argument presented by MacKay which he calls 'logical indeterminacy' gives an adequate account of human free will.[23] He says that 'even on the most physically-deterministic assumptions *there does not exist* a complete and detailed specification of my future with an unconditional claim to my assent'.[24] Maybe not, but if my future can be precisely predicted and not communicated to me, this still seems to me to remove genuine free will and responsiblity. However, that said, it should be noted that both the 'dual action' and 'dualistic interactionist' views I have described are anti-reductionist. Neither gives us any grounds for believing that a description of the brain alone in molecular terms is adequate scientifically to encompass all that makes us human. We are back to multi-level descriptions and emergence.

None of this is to say that minds could exist without brains. As pointed out earlier, minds are emergent features of brains, arising when a particular level of complexity is reached in the evolutionary chain, and not explicable solely in terms of lower level concepts. What we are saying is that minds are not to be identified with brains. Of course, remembering Haldane's argument which we met in Chapter 5 (and have now found re-iterated in different ways by Eccles and Popper), if minds *were* to be identified with purely mechanical neurophysiological events, then we would have no reason for believing our beliefs to be true — and in particular no reason to believe our discovery about the identity of mind and brain!

As I discuss below, the Christian view of man is as a psychosomatic unity rather than a disembodied soul. The discoveries of modern science, as well as the philosophical arguments I have discussed above, would seem to accord well with this traditional Christian view.

The Selfish Gene, Original Sin
and the Nature of Man

It's them as take advantage that get advantage i' this world.

(George Eliot, *Adam Bede*, Chapter 32.)

We have already encountered zoologist Richard Dawkins's view that we are 'gene survival machines'. Human behaviour, as animal behaviour, is programmed by the genes. We exist solely to propagate those genes.

This view fails to take into account the properties that emerge with higher levels of organization of matter that we see in the brain as discussed above. We have seen that scientifically mind events are not determined in any straightforward way by brain events, but there is a two-way causal connection. Moreover, the development of self-awareness and, very much associated with that, of language, provides man with a moral sense and a capacity to choose.

Even if there were a one-to-one correspondence between brain events and mind events, the insights of modern physics, notably the theory of chaos, (as described in Chapter 6), would free us from Dawkins's narrow mechanistic view. This is because there is an inherent unpredictability in the behaviour of complex systems like the human brain. Freedom of the will is something which modern physics allows which classical physics did not. Ironically, biologists like Dawkins seem to be adopting a mechanistic view of nature just as modern physics is discarding such a view.

Nevertheless there is something in the selfish gene picture which is in accord with traditional Christian theology.

Dawkins himself describes how two clergymen independently approached him after the publication of *The Selfish Gene* seeing the doctrine of original sin mirrored in the book.[25] Surely these clergy have a point.

It is very interesting that the way Darwinian evolution works is through a mechanism of selfishness — the survival of the fittest in a competitive world. This selfishness is undoubtedly in the genes, in man no less than in the rest of nature. In Dawkins's expression we are 'gene survival machines', though I have taken issue with his assertion that this is all we are. Of course, it is foundational to Biblical doctrine that man is selfish — this is the meaning of the Garden of Eden story. Taking the fruit of the tree of the knowledge of good and evil is the first act of disobedience to God. From it follows the loss of innocency: the human pair realize that they are naked; they are expelled from the beautiful garden; soon Cain kills his brother Abel; and so the sorry tale goes on. Time and again the Bible asserts man's sinfulness and his need of the redemption which ultimately only Christ can bring.

The Bible and evolutionary theory are in fundamental agreement on man's selfish nature. Both, too, recognise that man alone of the animals has the power to overcome that selfishness. Man is the only animal endowed with a self-conscious mind enabling him to choose freely whether to follow the selfish path or a nobler, altruistic way. We have seen the key rôle of language in this moral awareness. The other animals behave purely instinctively, as programmed by their genes, whether in preying on other species, or defending their own territory or competing aggressively against rivals of their own species for space, food or mating partners. Their behaviour can hardly be described as having any moral dimension at all. In contrast man, while possessing such drives and instincts, does not have to obey them. He has a moral sense, a conscience, and is able to distinguish between right and wrong.

Actually, my description of the animal world above is somewhat one-sided, for even there a kind of altruism operates, albeit one which we are coming to understand on the 'selfish gene' picture. Richard Dawkins describes how this works, basing his case on the two seminal papers of W. D. Hamilton[26] (major contributors since Hamilton include Maynard Smith and E. O. Wilson). Essentially, it is possible to calculate the relatedness of any two members of a family, and hence the extent to which it might pay any individual, in exchange for expenditure of its own energy and resources, to help another. As J. B. S. Haldane remarked, 'I'd lay down my life for two brothers or eight cousins.'[27] The point is that a brother shares half of your genes, a cousin one eighth and so on. Hence it profits *your* genes if you help near relations. An example cited by Dawkins is the saving from drowning of babies and injured whales by other members of a school, which have a high chance of being related.[28] Of course the animals do not do any sums to calculate relatedness, but natural selection favours behaviour which is altruistic to the right degree.

Perhaps this aspect of evolutionary biology also has something to teach us about human nature — certainly many scientists think so. As well as selfishness, our genetic make-up also programmes a certain degree of altruism. Theologically speaking, man is not 'totally depraved' as a result of the Fall, as Calvin taught. A right assessment of man will take into account both the seriousness of sin and his inherent capacity for good; it will also take account both of his genetic make-up and the genuine freedom of the will and moral sense which are his God-given higher-level attributes.

This brings me on to another area of science besides evolutionary biology which sheds light on man's nature, particularly his selfishness. The discipline of depth psychology has identified how our conscious minds repress certain feelings and emotions. This gives rise to an inner conflict between the conscious and unconscious elements of the 'self'. This conflict is very similar to that described by St. Paul in Romans 7:19-20:

> For the good that I would I do not: but the evil which I would not, that I do. Now if I do that I would not, it is no more I that do it, but sin that dwelleth in me.

Of course, the language of sin is not that of depth psychology, but, as pointed out by Christopher Bryant,[29] what is being described — the conflict between a conscious intention and a reaction from the unconscious — is very similar. Interestingly, as I discuss later in Chapter 10, the founder of modern analytic psychology, C. G. Jung, found with his patients, just as did St. Paul, that the resolution of such conflicts was only to be found in a spiritual awakening.

Modern science, whether it be neuroscience, evolutionary biology with its generation of emergent properties, or depth psychology, lends support to the idea of man as a psychosomatic unity. This is further exemplified by the trend towards 'holistic' medicine, particularly the greater awareness that physical illnesses can have a psychological basis. This too is how Christian doctrine sees man. The idea of the disembodied soul is in fact more Greek than Christian — Plato thought the soul could exist without the body, indeed pre-existed the body. Conversely, the body has been accorded great weight in Christianity (in contrast to other religions as well as Greek thought). Thus the resurrection accounts go to great pains to show that Christ was raised bodily from the dead. You will remember that he displayed his wounds for Thomas to feel, and that he is also portrayed as eating before his disciples (Luke 24:43). 'I believe in the resurrection of the body' is a clause of the Apostles' creed.

The Christian view is contiguous with the Hebrew view of the Old Testament. The latter has been well expressed by Wheeler Robinson, who, having surveyed the various terms used (soul, spirit, heart, flesh) concludes: 'The final emphasis must fall on the fact that the four terms (including that for "flesh") simply present different aspects of the unity of personality. The Hebrew idea of personality is that of an animated body, not (like the Greek) that of an incarnated soul'.[30] The present Archbishop of Canterbury, Dr George Carey, is also keen to emphasise that man is not compartmentalized into soul, spirit and body.[31] The Biblical doctrine is not that man has a soul but rather that he is a soul. So here again, in seeing man as a body-soul unity, we see a convergence of the modern scientific view and the Biblical view.

Man as a computer

You're not a man, you're a machine.

(George Bernard Shaw, *Arms and the Man*, Act III.)

Another aspect of Richard Dawkins's writing I should like to comment on is his constant use of the language of computer technology to describe the human brain. Thus he describes the optic nerve as 'wires leading from a bank of three million photocells to the computer that is to process the information in the brain'.[32] Although on the very first page of *The Blind Watchmaker* he says that he will treat computers as biological objects,[33] it is perhaps his tendency to treat humans as computers that is more worrying. Thus he speaks of the evolution of the brain in terms of an 'electronic arms race'.[34]

In using the language of information technology, Dawkins is picking up on another attempt in recent years from a direction different from biology, namely computer science, to describe the brain as a mechanism. The claim of *Strong Artificial Intelligence* (AI) is that the brain is a digital computer, albeit a rather sophisticated one. This claim has gained credence with the great advances made in computer technology. There are many things a computer can do much better than a human being — for example, carry out complex calculations with perfect accuracy and lightning speed and play chess (still not quite beating the top grand masters, however). We have designed robots to carry out repetitive tasks, such as on a production line. Progress is being made with computers that speak, and so on. In principle there is nothing to stop us designing a computer with which we can talk intelligently and which to all intents and purposes behaves in a totally human way. The only difference between the computer and a human will be the 'hardware' — humans are made of flesh and blood, but computers are made of metal. The 'software', or the program which controls the computer, will be very similar for each.

Roger Penrose[35] argues that if a computer with the appropriate program says 'I feel pain' or 'I love you', we must take these statements to be as real as if they were made by humans, and we must apply human moral concepts to our dealing with computers. In fact it is possible to draw the opposite conclusion, for, if true, the above picture will again be destructive for humanity and for a religious perspective on life. For if we humans are nothing but computers programmed in a special way, then our reason, our emotions, love and aesthetic feelings and so on, are all meaningless. Morality has no basis in a purely mechanistic universe.

Alan Turing who devised a test to decide whether a computer could 'think'. He postulated an interrogator asking the same questions of both a computer and a human being. The computer and the human would be hidden from view and their answers would be conveyed back type-written to the interrogator, so that the mere medium in which they replied would not give the game away. The aim of the interrogator would be to distinguish machine from man from the answers given to his questions.

There has been some success with programming computers to pass restricted forms of the Turing test, eg the simple story quoted by Penrose of a man going into a hamburger restaurant. The story can go several ways, eg the man buys a hamburger but leaves the restaurant angrily without paying his bill, or he pays his bill and gives the waitress a large tip. Testing questions are put. For example, the question 'Does he eat the hamburger?' should get the answer no in the first case and yes in the second, since, although this is not stated in either case, it is a sensible inference to draw from the circumstances. And we can see that a computer might be programmed to give sensible answers about such a story. The question is, even if computers could pass a genuine, full Turing test, would this show that they can think?

The philosopher John Searle[36] refutes this 'behaviourist' view that appearing to think would be identical with thinking by postulating a 'Chinese room'. He envisages a man locked in a so-called 'Chinese room' with questions coming into the room in Chinese and answers to be output in Chinese. The man in the room has a set of instructions in English about how to manipulate Chinese symbols in the light of the incoming questions in order to post answers back out of the room. It is a purely formal, mechanical procedure, just shuffling symbols according to the rule-book, that the man in the Chinese room goes through.

It is clear that the man in the room will not learn any Chinese using the procedures adopted. As Searle points out, the procedures he is adopting are purely *syntactical*; they have no *semantic* content. No understanding is involved in the execution of purely formal procedures. The contrast with the human mind is clear: here understanding is involved, and there is real content in human thought processes — they are actually about something.

The Chinese room example demonstrates very well the fundamental difference between how a computer operates and a human thinks. Essentially all a computer can ever do is *simulate* human behaviour. As Searle goes on to point out, it is really pretty ridiculous to confuse a simulation of something with the thing itself. We don't do it in other applications of computer technology, for example a computer simulation of cloud formation is not wet, nor does a computer simulation of a battle involve real explosions! So why do some proponents of artificial intelligence claim that computers which simulate thinking actually think?

There is another weakness in the argument that computers can think. This also follows from that fact that computers merely execute algorithmic procedures, ie pre-ordained sets of rules. It stems from Gödel's theorem, which we met in Chapter 6. You will remember that Gödel's theorem states that, in any mathematical system complex enough to include the whole numbers, there will be true statements which cannot be proved within the system. Thus we as human beings know things within these axiomatic systems which cannot be proved simply by stringing together chains of logical statements, which is all a computer can do.

Oxford philosopher J. R. Lucas has examined arguments which try to escape this conclusion and notes that they all fail.[37] For example, we might concede that a machine which is programmed to do arithmetic is inadequate to model the human mind because we can produce a Gödelian formula which we as humans know to be true but the machine cannot prove. So why not add this Gödelian statement to the machine's memory to make a more adequate machine? Of course, this still fails because we can produce a Gödelian formula in the new system which again the machine cannot prove. And no amount of adding new formulae to the machine's memory will make it immune to attack from human construction of a Gödelian formula.

Production of the Gödel formula is a standard procedure, as shown in my appendix. Suppose we make a machine with the usual operations of arithmetic *and* a 'Gödelian operator' for producing the Gödel formula successively for increasingly complex systems. It turns out that even this machine, which can generate an infinitude of further axioms using its Gödel operator, possesses the fatal weakness: there is still a statement which cannot be proved within the system which a human will be able to see is true. For the Gödel operator is of course a rule like any other which can be taken into account by the human in deriving a new Gödel formula.

Although this is all rather esoteric argumentation based on the niceties of pure mathematics, it does again reveal a fundamental difference between computers and humans — we can know things that computers can't and instantaneously seeing all the logical consequences of a set of axioms is a very limited capability compared with human knowledge.

Here again, in discussing strong AI, we have seen that the idea that man is a mere mechanism is refuted, and it is illuminating to see some of the differences between men and machines.

Consciousness, reason, understanding and a moral sense characterize human beings and nothing else we know of in this universe, whether it be beast or artefact. The dignity of man made in the image of God stands.

CHAPTER 8

The Retreat from Reductionism—
Some Alternatives

All are but parts of one stupendous whole,
Whose body nature is, and God the soul.

(Alexander Pope, *An Essay on Man.*)

We have seen in the preceding chapters that reductionism in science — 'nothing-buttery' — is a failure. It is a failure in its own terms in attempting to reduce all the higher level sciences to physics and mathematics, and it is a failure in its assertion that we are ultimately 'nothing but' atoms and molecules organized in a complex way through the process of evolution. It has failed to take into account the most recent developments in physics and mathematics, which move us away from a deterministic world of material particles for which we can find a complete explanation. It does not provide us with an explanation of those things which supremely make us human — the soul and its capacity for good and evil, love and hate, and its appreciation of beauty. On the other hand, reductionism is still widely believed and propagated. In this chapter I want to present and discuss three distinct reactions to this contradictory state of affairs.

The rejection of science

Modern man turns toward science, or rather against it, now seeing its terrible capacity to destroy not only bodies but the soul itself.

(Jacques Monod.[1])

One response to the appalling legacy of reductionism is to reject science altogether. This is the reaction of *Times* journalist Bryan Appleyard. In *Understanding the Present*[2] Appleyard makes an impassioned attack on the whole grand edifice of science. He presents a magisterial survey of the development of science since Galileo, and describes the inroads this new form of knowledge has made into traditional religious belief. He also shows how philosophers — from Descartes, Pascal, Kant and Kierkegaard up to Wittgenstein have attempted to come to terms with scientific knowledge. Appleyard presents the story as one of retreat for religious belief as science becomes the only available explanatory system, and the philosophers attempt to maintain the notion of the self against the rising tide of scientific discoveries and associated claims.

Appleyard argues that science has stripped man of his soul and destroyed any basis for an objective, absolute morality. In this context Appleyard makes a direct link between science and the concentration camps of Nazi Germany. Of course these were run on 'scientific' lines — the discoveries of science (eg nerve gas) were used for the clinical annihilation of the Jews in the Holocaust. Scientists were involved in experimentation on human beings in the camps (just as, we might note, they are today in embryo experimentation).

The philosophy of Nietzsche, with the elevation of the Superman as the striving hero in a universe in which God is dead, was a response to science. Morality as objectively given is abolished and man is a law unto himself. Even if unfairly, because he was only recognising the problem that science had presented us with, Nietzsche is seen as prefiguring Nazism — which, after all, did try to establish intellectual backing from him.

Much of Appleyard's analysis we can agree with. He decries the rhetoric of '"scientism" — the belief that science is or can be the only explanation'.[3] He describes science as 'an unprecedentedly effective way of understanding and acting' and goes on to say:

> We have seen that this way is intolerant, restless and ambitious,
> that it supplants religion and culture yet does not answer the needs

once answered by religions and cultures.[4]

Appleyard recognises the failure of attempts to reduce the human disciplines to natural science:

Nothing that can comfortably be called science has yet emerged from economics, politics and sociology.[5]

And again:

None of the so-called human sciences — anthropology, psychiatry, sociology — have achieved anything like the explanatory power of the science of nature.[6]

Marx, who attempted a scientific theory of history, made forecasts which were totally wrong — his theory has been comprehensively falsified. Appleyard believes that history is beyond the reach of science.

Appleyard also criticizes Freud who believed that 'our need for a single, all-powerful god was nothing more than the human psyche's need for a father'.[7] Appleyard regrets that there is nothing in such science 'to replace the beauty and poignancy of the Christian myth'[8] and clearly sees the religious need of man:

It is clear that there is something about the human condition that demands a dimension we call religious, whatever it might be.[9]

We are reminded of St Augustine's words, 'Thou hast created us for thyself, and our heart knows no rest, until it may repose in thee.' Sadly, however, albeit as it seems to me reluctantly (and, I would add, unnecessarily), Appleyard rejects a religious outlook. He appreciates that for some such an outlook will still work in the scientific age, but for him it will not. Rather, his is a 'pre-religious argument for non-religious people.'[10]

Appleyard insists, however, that the human soul is something irreducible, that morality is real and objective, and that it is worked out in the day to day personal relationships we have with our fellow men. He arrives at this point by invoking Wittgenstein's studies of language. Wittgenstein famously argued that there could be no such thing as a private language, that language is inherently social. This insight liberates man from the loneliness imposed on him by Descartes, who severed the solitary self, as being the only thing of which we could be certain, from its surroundings. As we noted in Chapter 5, it is very significant that Stephen Hawking dismissed philosophical studies of language in *A Brief History of Time*.

An author neglected by Appleyard who would have provided him with additional insight is the Jewish philosopher Martin Buber.[11] Buber distinguished the *I-It* relationship from the *I-Thou*. The former of these is the Cartesian detachment of self from objects, to which we have referred earlier, whereas the latter requires personal encounter and involves risk and openness to the other. It is the capacity for the *I-Thou* relationship which confers unique dignity and personhood on human beings. In terms of the main focus of this book, the *I-Thou* relationship is strongly anti-reductionist, requiring as it does total commitment: 'The primary word *I-Thou* can be spoken only with the whole being.'[12] It characterizes, of course, both man to man relationships and those between man and God, the 'Eternal Thou'.

Although much of Appleyard's analysis is appealing, I believe that he is ultimately mistaken in rejecting science as a whole. First, from what I have said in Chapter 4, I do not see the history of the interplay of science and religion in quite the terms Appleyard does. It is no accident that many of the scientific giants were believing and practising Christians — believing themselves to be 'following in God's footsteps after him' in the words of Kepler. Right up to the present day, many of the great scientists have taken a spiritual, if not explicitly Christian, outlook — Einstein and Schrödinger for example. Then, it seems to me, he is taking 'scientism', or as he also describes it, 'hard science', to be equivalent to true science. As we have seen, true science is actually much humbler than the popular presentations of Hawking and Dawkins would have us believe: the theories we have are only ever 'tentative', the programme to reduce all the sciences to physics and mathematics is doomed to failure, and even if it were successful it could not give us a 'Theory of Everything'. While recognising the success of methodological reductionism in many spheres, we are not obliged to accept the philosophically dubious positions of epistemological and ontological reductionism. On the other hand, the idea of science as a genuine way of gaining knowledge, which is self-correcting, and leads to a tightening — if never perfect — grasp on reality, does seem to me to be inescapable.

To reject science when all we need reject is the philosophical baggage of reductionism is to throw the baby out with the bathwater. Thus we are not forced to abstain from administering vaccines to the third world — Appleyard seems to imply that Western medicine diminishes the people and destroys their culture, by humiliating their local wisdom, ultimately depriving them of their souls. No, we can accept the benefits of science while keeping the more grandiose claims of its reductionist propagandists in their place.

While I have given considerable space to discussing Appleyard's views, it should be recognised that he is not alone in criticizing science. Before moving on, brief mention should be made of Mary Midgley, from whose well-reasoned *Science as Salvation*[13] I quoted in Chapter 1. As we saw then, Midgley is critical of science for answering the 'how' question and pretending that this is the same as the 'why' question; both Dawkins and Hawking are guilty of this. She is also critical of inflated claims fom scientists that 'Complete knowledge is just within our grasp'.[14] Now is not the first time that physics has been thought to be near completion. A particular feature of Midgley's book is its criticism of science offering 'salvation' through an eventual colonization of space by intelligent life. This idea from so-called 'physical eschatology' was discussed by Barrow and Tipler — intelligence transfers itself to ever more exotic forms of matter as the universe tends towards its final 'omega point'.[15] But again, in all these areas, it is important to differentiate between philosophical speculation and established theory, and between 'scientism' and true science.

Quantum mysticism

All things began in order, so shall they end, and so shall they begin again; according to the ordainer of order and mystical mathematics of the city of heaven.

(Sir Thomas Browne, *The Garden of Cyrus*, 1658.)

A more promising response to reductionist claims is to recognise the changes that have taken place in modern science, some of which I have described earlier, to see in them the demise of the reductionist position, and to explore the consequences for one's overall world view. In *The Tao of Physics*[16] high energy physicist Fritjof Capra explores the similarities between modern physics and the Eastern mystical traditions.

Modern developments, especially quantum theory and the special and general theories of relativity, have revolutionized our understanding of many of the basic concepts of physics. Let us just remind ourselves of some of them:

(i)   Space and time are no longer to be considered separately but as a unified four-dimensional space-time continuum.

(ii)   The geometry of space-time is curved, being warped by the presence of matter.

(iii)   Matter and energy are interchangeable.

(iv)   Electrons, photons etc exhibit both particle and wave-like behaviour.

(v)   Because of the 'Uncertainty Principle' it is impossible to measure the position and momentum of a particle simultaneously.

(vi)   The Uncertainty Principle also implies that small amounts of energy can be 'borrowed' for small amounts of time — hence the vacuum is far from inactive and empty but seething with activity, particles spontaneously coming into existence and annihilating within the smallest fraction of a second.

(vii)   There is an inter-relatedness between all matter, as demonstrated by the Einstein-Podolsky-Rosen experiment in quantum mechanics and Mach's principle on the cosmological scale.

(viii) In quantum theory, the observer is inextricably bound up with the observations he makes — indeed he brings events into being through the act of observation. He is also of course, ultimately, a quantum system.

Capra draws a number of parallels between these discoveries and Eastern religious thought. To begin with, there is the idea of the unity of all things. It is of course the object of many of the Eastern traditions to attain, through meditation, the state of enlightenment (known, for example, as *nirvana* in Buddhism). In this state there is a freedom from self and an absorption into the 'ultimate reality'. Physics has shown the intrinsic unity of all things — space and time form a four-dimensional continuum; Mach's principle demonstrates the dependence of terrestrial phenomena on the distant galaxies; the EPR experiment shows that quantum effects are effective at great distances; and observation of quantum events shows that the observer is inextricably bound up with the observed.

Many of the concepts of modern physics have a paradoxical quality — particle-wave duality and so on. The Eastern mystics, especially perhaps the Taoists and the Zen Buddhists, deny that words can ever express ultimate truth. Many Zen masters transmit their teachings in *koans*, nonsensical riddles, perhaps the most famous of which is to ask the student to describe the sound of one hand clapping.

One of the most important notions in Chinese thought is that of the interplay of the polar opposites, *yin* and *yang*. These take many forms but essentially the idea is that the one grows at the expense of the other till it reaches its maximum, then subsides and gives place to its opposite. The whole process is repeated in endless cycles. Seasonal change, the movement from summer to winter and back again, is the paradigm. Here again there is a parallel with wave and particle duality — these concepts are undoubtedly contradictory in terms of classical physics. And there is a parallel too with the Uncertainty Principle — the more accurately we measure the position of a particle the less we know about its momentum and vice versa.

One of the images of importance to Capra is the famous dance of Shiva. This is a metaphor denoting endless cycles of birth, death, rebirth, destruction and creation. This he likens to the endless cycles of particle creation and annihilation in nature.

What are we to make of all this? Well, again there is of course some truth in what Capra has to say. One of the themes of this book is that the old mechanistic universe is dead and modern physics has replaced it with something far more supple and conducive to a spiritual outlook. The developments of modern physics are certainly, as stated above, such as to warrant a revolution in outlook. Reductionism is dead along with the mechanistic universe; there is room for freedom and the existence of the soul. Yet it seems to me that Capra's analogies are just that, analogies and not much more.

That is not to deny that Eastern mystics have some genuine insights into reality. Just as Sir John Eccles (and presumably the rest of us) knew that the billiard ball, Newtonian deterministic picture of reality was wrong when applied to human behaviour, because we actually *experience* free will, so the Eastern sages understand that life is paradoxical and that the spiritual quest is more important than the concerns of the material world. Mystical experience is not to be denied; it is common to both West and East (we shall return to the subject of religious experience in general in Chapter 10). However, as we have seen, it is in the West that science grew up and that not by chance.

Belief in a personal creator was central to the quest for understanding of the 'book of nature' as God's good creation. The Eastern mystics knew and know nothing of quantum physics and neither is it their concern to do so. In particular they know nothing of the complex mathematical formalism in which modern physics is couched. Statements like Capra's 'What Buddhists have realised through their mystical experience of nature has now been rediscovered through the experiments and mathematical theories of modern science'[17] really do not stand up to scrutiny. Not believing in a personal God, the Eastern mystics lack the motivation to more practical study of nature and, while stressing the spiritual, seriously under-value the material world. I would argue that here as elsewhere it is Western, Christian spirituality which has generally got the balance right between the two. Witness the tremendous charitable effort of Christian organizations as well as the pursuit of science in the West.

At a more detailed level, there are a number of criticisms which can be levelled at Capra's analysis. First, while it is true that observation in quantum theory affects the system being observed, it is a gross exaggeration to say, as I put it above, that reality is brought about by the observer. There *is* an underlying objective reality, as expressed by the wave function, and the electron does exist, even if we cannot say where it is or specify its motion. Also there is a clear distinction to be drawn between the experimental apparatus and the consciousness of the human observer; it is measurement by the former which forces wave function collapse. As Polkinghorne says, the alternative that 'photographic plates stored away at the end of an experiment only acquire a definite image when someone opens the drawer to have a look at them' seems scarcely credible.[18] Polkinghorne goes on to quote, very appositely in this context, Ronald Knox's famous limerick on idealism:

> There was once a man who said 'God
> Must think it exceedingly odd
>   If he thinks that this tree
>   Continues to be
> When there's no one about in the Quad.'

And the anonymous reply:

> Dear Sir, Your astonishment's odd:
> I am always about in the Quad.
>   And that's why the tree
>   Will continue to be,
> Since observed by Yours faithfully, God.

No, what is observed in a quantum mechanical experiment relates to an objective reality. Moreover, what can be observed is limited — it is not the case that anything can happen when an observation is made. It is thus far from being the case that the quantum world evaporates away into undifferentiated nothingness akin to Buddhist conceptions of ultimate reality. Capra's statement that ultimately 'the structures and phenomena we observe in nature are nothing but creations of our measuring and categorizing mind' is plain false.

The second law of thermodynamics negates Capra's analogy with endless cycles of birth, death and so on. The universe is in reality winding down. Increasing entropy gives a definite arrow to time — as we noted earlier, cups fall from tables and break but broken cups do not spontaneously reconstitute themselves and fly back up to table-tops!

Capra illustrates the danger of hanging a metaphysical outlook too closely on current scientific theories which are liable to change. Thus he says, speaking of the breakdown of the simple particle picture of the constitution of matter:

> All these developments strongly indicate that the simple mechanistic picture of basic building blocks had to be abandoned, and yet many physicists are still reluctant to do so. The age-old tradition of explaining complex structures by breaking them down into simpler constituents is so deeply ingrained in Western thought that the search for these basic components is still going on.[19]

Capra strongly advocates the so-called 'bootstrap theory' whereby, in a well-defined sense, particles are infinitely divisible and are constituents of each other. A simple example might be that particle A comprised B and C, B comprised A and C, and C comprised A and B. Quoting Sir Charles Eliot, Capra likens the idea to statements in Mahayana Buddhism:

> In the heaven of Indra, there is said to be a network of pearls, so arranged that if you look at one you see all the others reflected in it. In the same way each object in the world is not merely itself but involves every other object and in fact is everything else. 'In every

particle of dust, there are present Buddhas without number.'

Unfortunately the bootstrap theory has declined in physics, the currently prevalent model asserting that there are indeed ultimate constituents of matter, namely quarks. The two models give different predictions and the quark model seems more in accord with experimental observation.[20]

Similarly Capra was dismissive of the notion of symmetry. In the East symmetry is 'thought to be a construct of the mind, rather than a property of nature and thus of no fundamental significance.'[21] Moreover he goes on to say:

> It would seem, then, that the search for fundamental symmetries in particle physics is part of our Hellenic heritage which is, somehow, inconsistent with the general world view that begins to emerge from modern science.[22]

On the contrary, the most powerful theories describing particle interactions in modern physics, the so-called gauge theories, are 'predicated entirely upon symmetries' to quote John Barrow.[23] Again Capra relied too heavily on the state of physics prevailing when he was writing.

In the light of this weight of criticism, one can but conclude that quantum mysticism is a blind alley.

The living Earth

> And from this chasm, with ceaseless turmoil seething,
> As if this earth in fast thick pants were breathing,
> A mighty fountain momently was forced.
>
> (Samuel Taylor Coleridge, *Kubla Khan*.)

Another reaction to scientific reductionism, and a contrasting holistic approach, arising within modern science has been the Gaia hypothesis of James Lovelock. The hypothesis arose out of Lovelock's work for NASA, where he was asked to devise an experiment to determine whether or not there was life on Mars. He suggested that the key test for life should be the composition of the atmosphere: a planet with life would have a very different atmosphere from one without life. Moreover, a test for atmospheric composition could be carried out anywhere on the planet: it would not depend on the particular landing site — indeed this particular test could be carried out from the Earth with no need for an expensive expedition. Taking the Earth as model, Lovelock concluded that the atmospheric composition has to be biologically determined. For example, methane and oxygen in the atmosphere react chemically in the presence of sunlight to give carbon dioxide and water vapour. These gases must be replenished at a phenomenal rate in order to maintain the abundances observed — and the only means to achieve the required rates of production are biological. Other gases (nitrous oxide, ammonia and even nitrogen which forms 78% of the atmosphere) are also unexpected constituents of the atmosphere today and should, in the absence of life, have oxidized away long ago. As Lovelock says:

> The chemical composition of the atmosphere bears no relation to the expectations of steady-state chemical equilibrium.[24]

The point is that in four and a half billion years, in the absence of life, the atmosphere should have come into chemical equilibrium, ie stabilized in a state such that no further chemical reactions can take place to produce energy. The principal components of an equilibrium atmosphere can be calculated: 99% carbon dioxide and 1% of the inert gas argon. This is to be compared with the very different composition we observe: 0.03% carbon dioxide, 78% nitrogen, 21% oxygen and 1% argon. Only the argon content is the same and that is because argon does not react chemically! Interestingly, infra-red observations of Mars in the 1960s showed that its atmosphere was predominantly (95%) carbon dioxide, close to the equilibrium value, and therefore incapable of supporting life.

Lovelock's conclusion from this, and similar considerations embracing the oceans and land surface composition, is the Gaia hypothesis. Gaia is the Greek name for the earth goddess and was suggested to Lovelock by his neighbouring villager, William Golding. The hypothesis is, quite simply, that the Earth can be regarded as a single living organism. More precisely, the biosphere is a self-regulating system which controls and maintains the conditions for life. It is important to recognise that this in complete contrast to the traditional view whereby the planet provides conditions for life: according to Gaia it is life which gives rise to the planetary conditions we observe and controls them.

Delving a bit further into this, we are told that the biosphere acts like a *cybernetic control system*. Lovelock gives the simple example of a thermostatically controlled oven to illustrate the idea. When the oven is turned on the temperature at first rises. The thermostat recognises when the temperature has risen above that set and then switches off the power. When the temperature falls below that set, this is again recognised by the thermostat and the power is switched on again. The temperature thus oscillates above and below the setting. From the point of view of reductionism Lovelock's comments here are particularly interesting:

> Think again about our temperature controlled oven. Is it the supply of power that keeps it at the right temperature? Is it the thermostat, or the switch that the thermostat controls? Or is it the goal we established when we turned the dial to the required cooking temperature? Even with this very primitive control system, little or no insight into its mode of action or performance can come from analysis, by separating its component parts and considering each in turn, which is the essence of thinking logically in terms of cause and effect. The key to understanding cybernetic systems is that, like life itself, they are always more than the mere assembly of constituent parts. They can only be considered and understood as operating systems. A switched off or dismantled oven reveals no more of its potential performance than does a corpse of the person it once was.[25]

We can see here very strong echoes of our earlier discussion in Chapter 5 of methodological and epistemological reductionism. Methodological reductionism, while unimpeachable philosophically, is inadequate by itself to understand phenomena — a complementary, holistic approach is also needed. Epistemological reductionism is an optimistic assumption rarely if at all attainable: while the parts obey the laws of physics appropriate to them, when combined we see new, emergent phenomena which we could not have predicted from the lower level laws. This seems to apply even to a machine.

We need a new language to describe these emergent phenomena — in the case of cybernetics we speak of 'negative feedback loops'. These are the links in a system which regulate it. Thus as the temperature in an oven rises the power is cut to reduce it and *vice versa*.

Lovelock thinks that the earth regulates its temperature and other physical attributes (composition etc) in a similar way to the oven using cybernetic feedback loops, although of course the whole business is more complicated than in the simple case of an oven. For example, he states that 'the biosphere actively maintains and controls the composition of the air around us so as to provide an optimum environment for terrestrial life.'[26]

Taking oxygen as his reference gas, he examines the function of the various other components of the atmosphere in its regulation. For example some billion tons of methane are disgorged into the atmosphere every year, largely by bacterial fermentation in muds, sea beds, marshes and other wet areas where carbon is buried. Unless the methane were produced and combined with oxygen the latter would build up at a rate of about 1% in 12,000 years. Bearing in mind that the current 21% is optimal for life and that a rise by as little as 4% would lead to a conflagration with unstoppable fires, such an increase would be catastrophic.[27] Lovelock postulates a control mechanism whereby an increase in oxygen concentration is 'sensed', and the proportion of carbon buried as opposed to turned into methane altered to restore the balance.

The Gaia hypothesis is a scientific theory. Richard Dawkins has attacked it because he does not see how life, as governed by the selfish gene, can co-operate to regulate the environment. Natural selection operates at the level of the individual gene. Genes which survive and reproduce are those which make their host organisms better adapted to their environments. If organisms produce oxygen it is not for the general benefit of the planet but because it is useful for themselves or a waste product of some process that is useful for themselves; otherwise mutants would arise which did not waste energy producing oxygen and these cheaters of the system would have enhanced survival probability. Dawkins challenges Lovelock to produce a model of a self-regulating Gaia.[28]

In true scientific spirit, Lovelock has not dismissed this criticism out of hand, but rather taken it as a spur to expound Gaia more accurately and to demonstrate how the hypothesis is compatible with Darwinian evolution — indeed, rising to the challenge, to produce a model.

Dawkins illustrates Darwinian evolution using a simple mathematical model involving 'biomorphs', geometrical structures on a computer screen which mutate, reproduce and are selected to survive according to certain rules. Similarly, Lovelock has invented 'Daisyworld' as a very simple model to illustrate how Gaia might work, and to allay at least some of the doubts scientists have about the theory. Daisyworld is a planet containing two types of daisy coloured dark and light. Colour determines the proportion of incident light reflected (technically the *albedo* of the surface). Dark coloured daisies absorb more light and reflect less than light coloured ones. The bare ground has a colour somewhere between that of the two varieties of daisy. The mean temperature of the planet is determined simply by the average colour. There is a range of temperatures suitable for daisy growth with the optimum somewhere in the middle of the range. The progress of the planet is followed from a time of low luminosity of its illuminating star to high luminosity. At first dark daisies are favoured because they warm the planet — eventually they colonize it. Then, when the temperature has risen above the optimum, light daisies start to predominate because they can keep cool. Eventually all daisies die when the star's luminosity becomes too high to cope with and the planetary temperature goes above the maximum allowed. Interestingly, despite the inexorably rising heat output of the star, the temperature of the planet is controlled at an almost constant value for a long period. This is in complete contrast to a traditional model in which life has no influence on the environment but merely adapts to it: then the temperature of the planet rises proportionately to the star's luminosity, and daisies die out far sooner.[29]

In response to biologists who claimed that cheating varieties of daisy would evolve and prosper, Lovelock has included a third variety in his model: grey daisies which do not use energy to make pigment. Having put in an energy penalty for the dark and light daisies for pigment production, Lovelock again ran his model. Still the temperature was well controlled. Dark daisies prospered first as before and light daisies last, with the grey daisies prospering in the middle around the optimum conditions.

Further features of variants of the Daisyworld model include much greater stability than traditional ecological models which tend to show much wilder fluctuations in the populations of species. Also, if perturbations such as plagues, wiping out large populations, are applied to the models, rapid evolution of species is observed followed by long periods of stability. Lovelock thus sees the models as according well with the punctuated equilibrium variant of evolution as favoured by Gould and Eldredge, rather than the 'standard' theory advocated by Dawkins and others.

We are thus beginning to see Gaia as a true scientific theory, as I have said. It makes predictions which are different from those of other theories and which can be tested, eg it has been verified that there is no life on Mars. Although Lovelock is regarded as something of a crank in the orthodox scientific community, his theory certainly cannot be dismissed lightly and will have to be tried in the fires of the scientific method. As yet I think we should say that the 'jury is still out' and no final verdict can be given. Meanwhile, what is the relevance of the theory to the main thrust of this book?

First Gaia is a holistic theory. It sees the Earth as a single organism; as Lovelock says, the 'properties of the planet could not be predicted from the sum of its parts.' Secondly, whether the theory itself is right or wrong, Lovelock has highlighted some very significant facts pertinent to man's existence on earth. Thus there are some very remarkable processes going on, governed by algae and the like, without which we could not be here, and many of the parameters of the environment are 'finely-tuned' for us to be here. Thus the oxygen content of the atmosphere is maintained at an optimal 21%, whether by the methane release/carbon deposition mechanism described earlier or otherwise — a rise to 25% would result in catastrophe. Similarly, the salinity of the sea is maintained at 3.4% — a rise to 6% would destroy life on earth.

One of the most interesting findings concerns the iodine cycle. Iodine is a trace element essential to the operation of the thyroid gland and without which most animals would die; it is gathered from the sea by kelp and then released to the air, and thence to the land. As Bishop Hugh Montefiore has observed,[30] these properties seem contrived for man's existence, just like Popper's preestablished harmonies which we met in Chapter 5, and the more general anthropic coincidences in astrophysics which we shall discuss in Chapter 9.

There is another direction still in which Gaian thought can lead us, more directly spiritual. Lovelock expresses his religious views in the final chapter of his second book on Gaia. He cannot bring himself to espouse any credal form of religion, though he does 're-spect the intuition of those who believe' and says, 'I am moved by the ceremony, the music, and most of all by the glory of the words of the prayer book that to me are the nearest to perfect expression of our language'[31] — feelings with which I fully concur.

Lovelock is, nevertheless, religious in the broader sense. He has something of the religious feeling of awe before nature expressed by Einstein which I quoted in Chapter 3. Of course the very name Gaia has religious, if pagan, associations. Lovelock clearly has great reverence himself for Gaia, and speaks of 'the whole planet cel-ebrating a sacred ceremony'. He likens Gaia to the Virgin Mary, close and manageable compared with the more distant Jahweh, and goes on to say:

> She is of this Universe and, conceivably, a part of God. On Earth she is the source of life everlasting and is alive now; she gave birth to humankind and we are a part of her.[32]

Some theologians have taken up the idea of the world as 'God's body'.[33,34] We can see the analogy with the human body — a complex organization of matter with a mind which interacts with and works through that body. We have seen that the mind is not to be identified with physical, brain processes but that the mind can control those processes. Similarly, the world is a highly organized complex system through which God might express his will. This would capture the Christian doctrine of the immanence of God, the belief that God is present in his universe. It would also capture the idea of God's vulnerability, again an important feature of Christian theology. That God made himself vulnerable in creating the universe and in giving freedom to his creatures, and that he also voluntarily limited himself in creation. The idea also has implications for the awe and respect we should have for the natural world.

Despite all this (and some of these insights are of undoubted value), I feel that the idea of the world, or the universe, as God's body is hardly to be justified. First, it would be a gross extrapolation from a scientific theory like the Gaia hypothesis to conclude that because the Earth seems to be alive it is the body of God. Secondly, it does rather smack of paganism (mother Earth goddess) and, I think not unconnected with this, seems to appeal to feminist theologians with a particular axe to grind — the reaction against God the Father, Biblical patriarchy and so on. Above all it contradicts traditional Christian theology: 'God is a Spirit: and they that worship him must worship him in spirit and in truth' (John 4:24). And as King Solomon prayed at the dedication of the temple, 'Behold, heaven and the heaven of heavens cannot contain thee' (1 Kings 8:27). While God is indeed immanent in the world, and I hope to show in Chapters 9 and 10 can and does act within it (perhaps in an analogous way to mind on matter), the idea of the world being his body undervalues that second great property of God, his transcendence: God is separate from and outside his creation. The point has been well made by C. S. Lewis:

> To say that God created Nature, while it brings God and Nature into relation, also separates them. What makes and is made must be two, not one. Thus the doctrine of creation in one sense emp-

ties Nature of divinity. How hard this was to do and, still more, to keep on doing, we do not now easily realise.[35]

The name Gaia is unfortunate in that it lends itself to the modern trend towards a re-deification of nature. Anthropomorphic expression of the theory in terms of the Earth as a living organism leads in the same direction. But talk of geophysiology and a cybernetic control system would perhaps not have the same ring to it! As Lawrence Osborn has pointed out,[36] we need to distinguish carefully between the scientific hypothesis and the myth attached to it.

In any case it is not necessary to adopt such a pantheist view of the world as God's body, Gaian-derived or otherwise, in order to justify reverence for nature. Orthodox Christian belief, according to which nature is God's good creation, sufficiently motivates care for the world over which man has been appointed steward.[37,38] The doctrine of the Incarnation is the ultimate ground for a proper appreciation of the material. It is towards the themes of orthodox Christian belief that I should like to move as this book draws to a close, but first, as a precursor, it is necessary to examine the rationale for theism, the belief in God as designer and creator of the world.

CHAPTER 9

Was the World Designed?

There are more things in heaven and earth, Horatio, than are dreamt of in your philosophy.

(*Hamlet*, Act 1, Scene v, line 166.)

The key questions we shall be looking at in this chapter are: Does God exist? Did he make the universe? Does he act within it?

We have seen in Chapter 1 how Richard Dawkins believes that, in the light of the theory of biological evolution, 'we don't need to postulate a designer in order to understand life, or anything else in the universe'.[1] We have also seen that Stephen Hawking sees God as purely a First Cause, the need for which is obviated if we can explain how the universe has no boundary in space-time. It might seem that in the light of modern science there is no room for God. Do we therefore stand with Laplace and say, 'I have no need of that hypothesis'?

We have already seen the serious shortcomings in the reductionist programme espoused by Dawkins and others, and that there are fundamental barriers to what we can know through science, removing Hawking's quest of a Theory of Everything to the realm of fantasy. We have looked at alternatives to reductionism and considered both the reassertion of personhood and the search for a more mystical approach to nature. I have stated that I do not see those alternatives as entirely satisfactory. I see the only plausible alternative as a return to the orthodox Christian belief which inspired the early scientific revolutionaries.

Yet there is still the vexed question of design, which we now need to look at more closely. Do scientific explanations, be they

155

necessarily incomplete, preclude God's involvement in design? Further, do they preclude his action in the world? The anti-reductionist arguments advanced so far would seem seriously to weaken such claims. However, there is in fact much more to be said positively in favour of the existence and activity of God.

In this chapter, we look briefly at some of the traditional arguments for God's existence, and then at one particular line of argument which has arisen directly, in the last few years, out of the modern science of cosmology. It is my aim to show that these arguments, while none of them in isolation is completely compelling, provide strong cumulative support for the thesis that God exists, and that he designed and made the world.

Since there is much misunderstanding of the impact of scientific discoveries in the realm of origins on Christian belief, we must consider briefly just what is asserted by the Christian doctrine of creation.

The Christian believes that not only does God exist but that he acts in the world he has created. In the later part of this chapter we go on to show that in the modern scientific picture of the world there is indeed room for God to act — in fact the modern view is much more encouraging in this respect than older, mechanistic views. In the next chapter, following a re-statement of the basic tenets of the Christian faith, I show that there is good reason to believe that God has acted very specifically in history, and still acts today in the world he has made.

Traditional arguments

> Whence is it that nature does nothing in vain; and whence arises all that order and beauty which we see in the world?
>
> (Sir Isaac Newton, *Opticks*, 1704.)

A number of philosophical arguments have traditionally been propounded for the existence of God. The ontological argument, formulated by St Anselm of Canterbury, begins by defining God to be 'something than which nothing greater can be conceived'. Anselm goes on to say that something which exists in reality is clearly greater than something which exists only in the mind. Therefore, God must exist, otherwise something greater, ie a being with existence in addition to God's other attributes, could be conceived.

This argument may strike the reader as somewhat too clever by half and therefore rather suspect. Can one really argue by juggling with words in this way, without considering anything material about the universe or even about what constitutes greatness, that God must exist? It may yet be that one can, and it may well be that God is a *necessary* being in the philosophical sense (to deny his existence is self-contradictory), but the weight of philosophical opinion is against the ontological argument. In particular Immanuel Kant argued strongly against it in the eighteenth century:

> It is absurd to introduce — under whatever term disguised — into the conception of a thing, which is to be cogitated solely in reference to its possibility, the conception of its existence.[2]

To summarize, Kant and his followers argued that the distinction between existence in reality and mere conception must be maintained; that existence is not a legitimate attribute of an entity in the same way as other attributes, eg greatness or colour; and that the application of such other attributes presupposes existence and vice versa.

The cosmological argument starts from the observation that there *is* a universe and asks, 'What is the explanation for the existence of this universe?' More simply still, as Leibniz put it, why is there something rather than nothing? The argument is that God is the ultimate ground of existence — the backward chain of causality stops with him. Science can only explain one state of the universe in terms of its causation by a previous state and the operation of the appropriate laws of nature. Such a mode of causation cannot explain the initial state of a universe of finite age, nor provide a cause outside itself for an infinite universe (nor of course for a finite universe with no 'boundary conditions'). However, there is a fundamental objection to the cosmological argument too, namely, why should there be an explanation of the universe's existence at all? Perhaps the universe is a given, brute inexplicable fact, and critics of the cosmological argument would say that this is as satisfactory a position as postulating a God who has no explanation.

The traditional argument from design points beyond the existence of the universe to certain striking features of it. These are that the universe exhibits a regularity and intricacy which are suggestive of its having been designed. One might cite as an example the way in which animals are perfectly suited to their environments, being able to gather food of the right sort and survive against predators; and all nature is balanced in this remarkable way. The classic formulation of the argument was by Archdeacon William Paley in the eighteenth century. Paley described a man walking across a heath and finding a watch on the ground. On examining the intricate mechanism of the watch the man would be struck by the idea that the watch was obviously designed by a clever watch-maker. How much cleverer the designer of the far more intricate hand holding the watch!

The problem with the design argument, at least in this form, is that we now know scientifically how nature came to be so delicately balanced and interwoven. Darwinian evolution shows how different species evolve through the mutation of genes and the selective survival of those better adapted to their environment. We have an alternative explanation, for which there is good scientific evidence, to the God-hypothesis. Richard Dawkins takes the title of his book, *The Blind Watchmaker*, from Paley's example, and, as we have seen, his central thesis is precisely that we and all creatures have been produced by the blind forces of evolution.

Thus it would appear that none of the traditional arguments, including that from design, work as knock-down proofs of God's existence. However, to see them in this way is in any case mistaken. Bearing in mind that science cannot prove its assertions (as we have seen in Chapter 3), it comes as no surprise that neither can theology. Rather, these arguments should be used as pointers or indicators towards God. Professor Richard Swinburne has shown in particular how the second and third arguments can be made much more rigorous in providing corroborative evidence for God's existence.[3]

Swinburne's approach is to formalize these arguments using the mathematical theory of probability. He thus attempts to get a handle on the probability that God exists given certain features of the universe, such as its very existence or the observed order within it. This he can do using a well-established theorem of probability theory due to the Rev Thomas Bayes. Bayes's theorem enables one to write down a formula for the probability that some hypothesis is true, given some piece of evidence under discussion, in terms of the *a priori* probability that it is true, ie the probability not taking into account this evidence. That is to say, the theorem shows how one should revise one's prior views in the light of evidence. We shall follow through Swinburne's arguments, providing the formula in the Appendix for the more mathematically minded!

It should be noted first, however, that the discipline of probability theory has not been without controversy. Indeed there has been much discussion about what precisely is meant by probability, in particular how the mathematical formulation relates to the real world. Rudolf Carnap[4] identifies two main interpretations, namely 'relative frequency' and 'logical', while other authors give four or more interpretations. Thus Roy Weatherford[5] adds the 'classical' and the 'subjective' interpretations to his classification. I shall discuss these approaches briefly, but inevitably also simplistically. The interested reader is referred to the literature for more detail; the non-mathematical reader is advised to skip over the next couple of paragraphs.

In the 'relative frequency' approach probability is empirical, based on repeated observations. Thus the probability that a tossed coin will land heads is the limit to which the proportion of heads in successive tosses tends as the number of tosses tends to infinity. This is the approach that is widely adopted in science and the one most mathematicians and scientists are brought up on. In the 'logical' approach probability is the 'degree of confirmation' of an hypothesis with respect to an evidence statement. Carnap has developed an inductive logic around this notion of probability, and it is this interpretation on which Swinburne relies. Mathematically, this probability can be derived as a ratio of a 'measure' on possible worlds or 'state descriptions' in which both the hypothesis and the evidence pertain to a similar measure on the worlds in which the evidence pertains (note that the set of worlds in which both hypothesis and evidence pertain is a subset of the set of worlds for which the evidence pertains). Here, measure is a technical term denoting a mathematical function with certain properties, especially that the measure of the union of sets with no common element is the sum of the measures for the individual sets. Measure theory forms the basis of the mathematical theory of probability.[6]

The classical approach, which is the fore-runner of the others (especially the logical), related probability to equally likely outcomes in games of chance (eg a single throw of a die will yield a five with probability one sixth). Subjective probability is a measure of personal degree of belief in a proposition, and can be obtained from a subject by ascertaining his preferences among gambles. This last interpretation is used especially in decision theory.

It should be noted that while there has indeed been controversy surrounding these different interpretations, Carnap himself thought that both the logical and relative frequency approaches which he discussed were valid; they were simply addressing different problems. Moreover, all the interpretations of probability give rise to the same probability calculus, ie all obey the mathematical axioms and their consequences. In particular, they obey Bayes's theorem. The real dispute about Swinburne's approach is whether probability as degree of confirmation is allowable and whether numbers can be obtained for the prior probabilities.

It is interesting that recently Bayes's theorem has been used to give quantitative substance to the Occam's razor type of choice among competing physical theories.[7] A chief feature of Swinburne's argument is his application of just such an Occam's razor type test to the hypothesis that God exists uncaused. He regards this as the simplest of hypotheses and therefore of higher prior probability than other hypotheses, such as the existence of an uncaused universe. By God, Swinburne means a being who has omnipotence and omniscience among his qualities. A being with infinite power and knowledge is simpler than one with a finite limited quantity of power or knowledge, because in the latter case one would have to ask, 'Why is the limit just what it is?' Similarly the existence of an uncaused universe is a complex hypothesis compared with the existence of an infinite being: it just cries out for an explanation.

In saying that the existence of God is a simple hypothesis and that of an uncaused universe a complex one, Swinburne parts company with Richard Dawkins. About beliefs in a deity Dawkins argues:

> All that we can say about such beliefs is, firstly, that they are superfluous and, secondly, that they assume the existence of the main thing we want to explain, namely organized complexity.[8]

He goes on to argue, in the same passage, that, in order to engineer all the organized complexity in the universe, 'that deity must already have been vastly complex in the first place'. Surely not, for on Dawkins's own reckoning, evolution by natural selection is an essentially simple hypothesis for producing complexity. Why therefore should God be complex? Swinburne argues that a person with infinite capacities is essentially simpler than one with finite capacities because, as we have said, in the latter case one is forced to ask, 'Why are these capacities limited to such and such particular values?' For example, a being who can both create and mould matter is simpler than one who can only mould it, like Plato's demiurge.

Swinburne argues that this is the same kind of simplicity that a gravitational attraction proportional to $1/r^2$ possesses over one proportional to $1/r^{2.000142}$. The latter is both unnatural and has physically unsatisfying consequences.[9] Following Dirac and Polanyi one would believe the $1/r^2$ law despite experimental evidence to the contrary (up to a point of course — certainly the reliability of the experiment would need to be plainly demonstrable to force abandonment of so pleasingly simple a law).

We shall see below how some are led to invoke distinctly uneconomical and complex hypotheses in order to avoid belief in God.

In the mean time, let us see how these ideas we have been discussing may be applied, first to the cosmological argument. Swinburne argues as above that the probability that a complex physical universe exists uncaused is very low, less say than the existence of God uncaused: there are a lot of questions one might want to ask about why a complex physical universe is the way it is (and we shall be examining some of them below). For all practical purposes we can say that the probability that there is a complex physical universe given the non-existence of God is the same as the probability of there being such a universe uncaused (this ignores the possibility that the universe was caused by some lesser being than God, one with say large but finite power, since as we have seen such a being is much less likely to exist than God).

Thus the probability that there is a complex physical universe given the non-existence of God is very low. In contrast, the probability that there is a complex physical universe given that there is a God, while not necessarily high, is much higher than the existence of such a universe if there is no God. This is partly because an infinite, omniscient, omnipotent being is likely to *use* his creative powers to realize good and value. More especially though, the probability that there is a universe given a God is higher than that given no God because a complex physical universe is extremely unlikely to exist uncaused.

It follows that the probability that God exists given the existence of a complex physical universe is greater than the *a priori* probability that God exists (ie in Swinburne's terminology the probability taking into account only background tautological knowledge). That is, the existence of a complex physical universe is good corroborative evidence for God's existence. It does not of course prove that God must exist, only that we have evidence in support of the hypothesis that he does.

To summarize: a complex physical universe is more likely to exist if God exists than if he does not (it is extremely unlikely to exist if there is no God). Therefore the observed existence of such a universe is corroborative evidence for the existence of God.

Richard Dawkins complains about those who make statements about the unlikelihood of life arising spontaneously: we must not accept things as *a priori* improbable, but should do the probability calculations. Yet he himself assumes *a priori* that God is improbable! In fact, as shown by a calculation I give in the Appendix, a low *a priori* probability for God's existence can be revised to a high probability for his existing given the evidence of a complex physical universe.

The argument from design can be treated in a similar way, though now we want to ask, 'Does the existence of order in the universe, given that a complex physical universe exists and other background tautological knowledge, further enhance the probability that God exists?' First, however, it is necessary to dispose of the proposition that Darwinian evolution explodes the design argument.

Evolution produces complex creatures out of simpler ones. But it works according to an orderly law of nature. Matter in all parts of the universe at all times obeys a few simple laws of physics. These laws of nature are endowed with remarkable fruitfulness in that they produce the complexity we observe from the simple beginning of the Big Bang. So what we ought to be examining when we think of order in the universe is not the delicate balance of nature but the laws of nature which brought about this delicate balance. These laws will include higher level laws which take over at increasing levels of complexity.

Swinburne argues that there is much more likely to be order of this kind if there is a God than if there is not. If there is no God then we are expected to believe that the orderliness of the universe, manifested in all matter at all times and in all places obeying the same set of laws, is a brute unexplained fact; and this seems extremely unlikely. Conversely, such order is extremely likely if it derives from a common source, just in the way that all tenpenny pieces are identical because they all come from the same mould. Thus order is very likely if there is a God. Moreover, if God produces a universe at all he is very likely to produce an orderly one rather than a totally disordered one because of his character. Swinburne argues that the properties of omnipotence, perfect goodness, and so on ascribed to God are essential to him and contribute to his simplicity. Creation of an ordered universe is a consequence of his goodness. The argument leads to the conclusion that the probability that God exists given an orderly complex physical universe is higher than the probability that he exists just given a universe and hence order in the universe is good corroborative evidence for the existence of God.

Other arguments can be invoked for the existence of God besides the basic ontological, cosmological and design (sometimes called *teleological*) ones we have looked at so far. We have seen that reason cannot have a scientific cause in the sense that it is derived from unreason — the blind interplay of the forces of nature on inanimate matter. We have further seen that the existence of morality — the concepts of good and evil — are not explicable in mechanistic scientific terms. Swinburne has applied the same type of Bayesian approach to these phenomena, gaining ever more corroborative evidence for the existence of God.

To summarize, it is possible to obtain evidence for the existence of God from what we can observe — that there is a universe, that it is ordered, and that in it are conscious, thinking beings who know the difference between good and evil. Of course, not many are persuaded to believe in God through purely philosophical arguments of this type. Christians put much more stress on God's own revelation of himself, supremely in Jesus Christ — and we shall return to this in the next chapter. Nevertheless, it is good to know that, not only do science and philosophy not preclude the existence of God, but they provide positive evidence in support of such a belief.

Before leaving the topic of philosophical arguments for the existence of God, we turn our attention to one notable development arising in very recent years out of modern cosmology.

Modern anthropic arguments

When I consider thy heavens, the work of thy fingers, the moon and the stars, which thou hast ordained; What is man, that thou art mindful of him? or the son of man, that thou visitest him?

(Psalm 8:3,4.)

New light has been shed in the last few years on the design argument by cosmologists who have asked how special the laws of nature must be in order to give rise to man. The *anthropic principle* states that there have to be constraints on these laws for them to produce men and it prompts one to examine just what these constraints are. In particular, John Barrow and Frank Tipler have written a monumental tome on this subject with the title *The Anthropic Cosmological Principle*,[10] but other writers too have addressed the subject (notably Paul Davies in *The Accidental Universe*[11]). Polkinghorne,[12-16] Swinburne,[17] Barbour[18] and Montefiore[19] have all assessed its impact on Christian apologetic.

By the laws of nature we mean Newton's laws of motion and gravitation as modified by Einstein's special and general theories of relativity; Maxwell's laws of electromagnetism governing the behaviour of charged particles; and quantum theory governing the behaviour of matter on the smallest scale. We think too of the four fundamental forces of nature — gravitation, electromagnetic forces between charged particles (which hold atoms together), the weak nuclear force giving rise to nuclear processes such as the decay of neutrons into protons, and the strong nuclear force binding the nuclei of atoms together. Of particular interest are the constants which govern the relative magnitudes of these forces and parameters such as the masses of the various fundamental particles such as the proton. The constants of nature (such as the Gravitational constant) and the masses of the various particles are necessary as inputs into the equations describing how matter behaves. The actual values they take are inexplicable by science. They are God-given, if you like, to use a term sometimes loosely used by the scientists themselves. Yet it turns out that they must take very precise values in order for the universe to be interesting and fruitful and to produce men.

The anthropic principle promotes man to his place at the centre of the universe from which he was demoted by Copernicus. Thus the universe needs to be the vast size it is in order for man to exist. This is the size it inevitably reaches in the 15,000 million years which we saw in Chapter 2 were necessary to evolve human beings — it must not re-collapse before this time. A universe with the mass of a single galaxy has enough matter to make a hundred billion stars like the sun, but such a universe would expand for only about a month.[20] Thus the argument that the vastness of the universe points to man's *insignificance* is turned on its head — only if it is so vast could we be here!

In Chapter 2 I described the cosmic expansion; the formation of stars and galaxies; the nucleosynthesis of the chemical elements inside stars; the enrichment of the interstellar medium with these elements following supernovae explosions; the formation of new generations of stars, and planets, from this enriched material; and the subsequent evolution of life culminating in man.

One of the most important elements necessary for our existence is hydrogen — no hydrogen means no water and hence no life. If the delicate balance between the weak nuclear force and gravitation were upset ever so slightly all the hydrogen would be converted to helium within a few seconds of the Big Bang.[21,22] Also, stars which burnt helium through nuclear reactions in their cores would be much shorter-lived than hydrogen-burning stars. Life would not have time to develop on the planets of such stars.

The magnitudes of the fundamental forces, especially the strong force and the electromagnetic force, are also critical to the way in which the nuclear reactions inside stars proceed. Life as we know it is based on the element carbon and it is unlikely that any other element could give sufficiently stable compounds to produce alternative life forms. It will be remembered that the chemical elements are built up inside stars. Carbon is one step on the way to building up all the other elements in the periodic table. We are required both to get as far as carbon in the first place and then, even more delicately, not to burn up all the carbon we have made to manufacture the other elements — we have to leave some behind! If the strong force and electromagnetic force were not so very finely balanced as they are we would get either no carbon in the first place or all the carbon would burn to make oxygen. This aspect of the anthropic argument is discussed both by Barrow and Tipler[23] and by Davies,[24] both following an argument of Fred Hoyle. We are reminded of Popper's discussion of preestablished harmonies which we met in Chapter 5.

One of the finest balancing acts necessary is the relative strength of expansion and contraction forces in the Big Bang. The earliest time we can sensibly talk about is the Planck time, 10^{-43} seconds after the Big Bang, before which an as yet unknown (but much sought after) theory of quantum gravity is required to describe the physics of the universe. An alteration of the ratio of expansion and contraction forces at this time by as little as 1 part in 10^{60} would lead either to too fast expansion with no galaxies forming or too slow expansion with rapid recollapse. (Incidentally, as Polkinghorne has pointed out, an accuracy of 1 in 10^{60} is about the same as that required to hit a coin situated at the other side of the universe 15,000 million light years away.) In a nutshell, the universes governed by these tiny alterations leave no room for interesting developments, and in particular the evolution of complex creatures like ourselves to observe them.

Another important factor is the amount of order in the universe. The second law of thermodynamics tells us that the universe is progressing from a state of order to states of increasing disorder. The amount of order in a system is measured in physics by a quantity called entropy — low entropy corresponds to a high degree of order and high entropy to high disorder. Now, the universe started in a state of almost incomprehensibly high order (or low entropy)[25]. Roger Penrose shows that, in starting the universe, the creator had of the order of

$$10^{10^{123}}$$

possible universes to choose from, only one of which would resemble ours.[26] The probability that a universe arising randomly would possess the necessary degree of order that ours does (and so possess a second law of thermodynamics) is

$$1 \text{ in } 10^{10^{123}}$$

As Penrose[27] points out, the number $10^{10^{123}}$ cannot even be written down in full. If we attempted to write 1 followed by 10^{123} noughts with each nought being written on a separate proton, with a mere 10^{80} protons there would not be nearly enough of them in the entire universe to be able to do this! This is fine-tuning indeed.

There is a very natural conclusion to draw from all this, namely that the cosmic coincidences we have been considering are indeed no accident: God designed the universe with the express intention of producing rational conscious beings with a moral sense, to contemplate his handiwork and to enter into a relationship with him.

Avoiding the obvious

Man, dreame no more of curious mysteries,
As what was here before the world was made,
The first Mans life, the state of Paradise,
Where heaven is, or hell's eternall shade,
For Gods works are like him, all infinite;
And curious search, but craftie sinnes delight.

(Fulke Greville, Lord Brooke, Sonnet lxxxviii.)

It would appear from the foregoing that something very contrived is happening for the universe to produce man, and it would seem very natural to infer that God is responsible. However, there are a number of ways of avoiding this conclusion. First, it may be that an improved cosmological theory will explain some of the coincidences. For example, if the universe underwent an early period of rapid, exponential expansion, as advocated in the 'inflationary' cosmologies first proposed by Alan Guth, then the expansion rate following the inflationary phase would settle very close to the critical value for a wide range of initial conditions. But the inflationary universe only arises if the laws of physics follow a certain pattern, and the 'anthropic fruitfulness' of such a universe is still to be explained.[28]

Another possibility is that our universe is not unique. Indeed, in order to deny design, it is necessary to postulate infinitely many universes in which such features as the universal constants are randomly selected for each. The idea is that, if there are infinitely many universes, one like ours is certain to be among them and hence it is no surprise that we are here. Now it must be emphasized, that while such an explanation is possible, it is not in any way a scientific explanation but, as Polkinghorne says,[29] a metaphysical one. We have only this universe to observe so speculation about others is metaphysical. So of course is the postulate of God's existence, but as Polkinghorne and Swinburne argue, this is a postulate of much greater economy and simplicity than an infinite ensemble of universes (Occam's razor again). The latter seems contrived to avoid the very natural conclusion of the former.

Having said that, and however implausible the many-universes hypothesis might seem, it must be recognised that it is at least a possible way to avoid the conclusion that our universe is contrived. What is required to transfer it from the realms of metaphysics to physics is some observational consequences. Dennis Sciama has in fact suggested that, under the many-universes hypothesis, 'we would not expect our universe to be a more special member of the ensemble than is needed for our development', whereas by contrast 'a unique universe might be expected to be very special indeed'.[30] Sciama points out that, in order to determine whether or not our universe is 'super special' we require a 'still-to-be-constructed measure theory on the ensemble space of the universes'. Such a measure theory would greatly improve the rigour of anthropic arguments by providing a basis for assigning probabilities to the parameters which describe the universes. (Note that Paul Davies has made a similar point to this in his book *The Mind of God*.[31])

Marginally more plausible than the infinitude of universes cited above is the idea that the universe is unique but spatially infinite, and we just happen to live in a region with the right parameters for anthropic potentiality. The inflationary hypothesis may explain the uniformity of our 'neck of the woods'. However, since we could have no causal contact with other regions in which the physical constants and initial conditions were different, this too is a metaphysical rather than scientific hypothesis. As before it would be of interest to examine just how special our part of the universe is.

Another argument advanced by some cosmologists against the existence of God should be considered here. This is that the universe may be uncaused in the sense that it came into existence spontaneously (something like this is envisaged by physical chemist Peter Atkins whom we quoted in Chapter 1). The argument comes from a consideration of the vacuum in quantum theory. Now, rather than being devoid of all matter, in quantum theory the vacuum is a sea of activity — particles and their anti-particles are spontaneously coming into existence and annihilating in a split second. This phenomenon arises from Heisenberg's Uncertainty Principle. We have seen that the position and momentum of a particle cannot be measured accurately simultaneously; similarly the energy contained within a given volume at a given time cannot be known for certain, with the consequence that energy can be 'borrowed' from the vacuum for a very short time. The possibility then arises of a quantum fluctuation of the vacuum in which many particles are created and separated from their anti-particles in the inflationary expansion of the universe, thereby not undergoing annihilation but continuing their existence. We effectively have creation of the universe *ex nihilo*!

A variant of this is Stephen Hawking's 'no boundary' universe, which he developed with fellow cosmologist Jim Hartle. In this theory, essentially what happens is that space-time is 'smoothed out' as one recedes to the Big Bang itself, so that no singularity at the origin is reached. To achieve this, Hawking and Hartle postulate a quantum mechanical wave function for the whole universe, a much-debated procedure fraught with philosophical as well as physical difficulties. For example, we have seen how the observer plays a critical rôle in the conventional quantum theory of the very small, but what rôle can there be for him when the entire universe is the quantum system under investigation? Furthermore, because the dimension of time is treated in the same way as the three spatial dimensions in this theory, time becomes imaginary at the earliest epochs (for the mathematically minded the word 'imaginary' is used here is in the technical sense of complex numbers). This clearly raises some difficulties of interpretation! Nevertheless, let us suppose for the sake of argument that some such theory is valid.

First, let us note in passing that these newer theories resemble the old steady-state theory in not assigning a definite beginning to time. Thus, in a sense, no new theological problem is raised that was not there with the steady-state theory.

In fact, however, it is quite erroneous to conclude, even if any of these rather speculative theories were true, that the universe is then uncaused and there is no need for God. It is the laws of nature which operate to produce the quantum vacuum fluctuation — where do these laws come from? Moreover, we are still very far from explaining all the cosmic coincidences necessary for such a universe to evolve and produce men. Indeed both the cosmological and design arguments still apply: the question why is still unanswered, and the order in the universe unexplained. But there is something more to say. The claim of Hawking and others, that if we can scientifically explain the origin of the universe (or show that it had no origin in time) we have removed the need for God, betrays an ignorance of the Christian doctrine of creation. So pervasive is this misunderstanding that it deserves a section of its own to clarify the matter.

The Christian doctrine of creation

He showed me a little thing, the size of a hazelnut, in the palm of my hand, and it was as round as a ball. I looked at it with my mind's eye and I thought, 'What can this be?' And answer came, 'It is all that is made.' I marvelled that it could last, for I thought it might have crumbled to nothing, it was so small. And the answer came into my mind, 'It lasts and ever shall because God loves it.' And all things have being through the love of God.

(Julian of Norwich.)

The Christian doctrine of creation is not dependent on a particular view of how God made the world or indeed whether the universe had a beginning in time. Even if the universe were of infinite age as in the steady-state theory, that would not matter since God is outside time anyway. Interestingly the proponents of the now defunct steady-state theory mistakenly thought they were doing away with God and had philosophical reasons for preferring their theory. Hermann Bondi is a well-known humanist (indeed he is currently President of the Rationalist Press Association); he has vigorously attacked religion, as has Fred Hoyle.

But, while the Bible asserts that God is creator, it is not concerned with *how* he created. You will remember Stephen Hawking's question, posed on consideration of a universe with no boundary or edge, neither beginning nor end, which we quoted in Chapter 1, 'What place, then, for a creator?' Polkinghorne has replied succinctly to this as follows:

> Within Christian theology, at least, it would be naive to answer that last question in any other way than 'every place'. The Creator is not the answer to the question 'Who lit the blue touch paper of the Big Bang?' God is not a God of the Edges, with a vested interest in boundary conditions. That is because the Christian doctrine of creation is concerned, not with *temporal* origin (how did things begin?) but with *ontological* origin (why is there anything at all?).[32]

Donald MacKay made exactly this point in a review of *The Blind Watchmaker*, providing one of his characteristic illustrations:

> Dawkins seems quite unaware that from the standpoint of biblical theism, as distinct from classical deism, the case for belief in the createdness of our world — its ontological origin in God's creative word — would not be strengthened by any conceivable failure on our part to trace the chronological origin of its present structure. When we say that a novel has an author, we do not imply that there are inexplicable discontinuities in the past of the world he has created; nor would the discovery of such things strengthen our belief in his authorship. The divine authorship of our world, according to theism, is what accounts for there being 'something rather than nothing' — regardless of its complexity.[33]

Precisely so. As St. John puts it, 'Thou art worthy, O Lord, to receive glory and honour and power: for thou hast created all things, and for thy pleasure they are and were created' (Rev 4:11).

Furthermore, this Christian doctrine of creation embraces much more than the granting of existence to the universe. God is upholding and sustaining the universe at every moment of its existence. As the writer to the Hebrews puts it (Hebrews 1:1-3), attributing this upholding to the second person of the Trinity:

> God, who at sundry times and in divers manners spake in time past unto the fathers by the prophets, Hath in these last days spoken unto us by his Son, whom he hath appointed heir of all things, by whom also he made the worlds; Who being the brightness of his glory, and the express image of his person, and upholding all things by the word of his power, when he had by himself purged our sins, sat down on the right hand of the Majesty on high.

St Paul too sees Christ as creator and sustainer:

> For by him were all things created, that are in heaven, and that are in earth, visible and invisible, whether they be thrones, or dominions, or principalities, or powers: all things were created by him, and for him: And he is before all things, and by him all things consist (Col 1:16,17).

Donald MacKay gives the analogy of a television programme.[34] We might be watching a tennis match from Wimbledon. The server tosses up the ball and serves, the receiver returns, and the world on the screen seems autonomous, independent of us outside it, and behaving in an orderly manner. Yet the picture is entirely dependent on the pattern formed by electrons hitting the cathode ray tube; and this pattern in turn depends on the modulating programme of signals controlling the electron beam. Alter the modulating programme and the pattern would be destroyed — indeed with the flick of a switch the picture is gone. Similarly, unless God were upholding the universe, it too would cease to exist. It is not the laws of nature which guarantee that we shall continue to go about our daily lives, but God who ordains that these laws continue to apply. As the great Christian evening hymn puts it, 'The day thou gavest, Lord, is ended, The darkness falls at thy behest'. Every day and every night, indeed every moment, is a gift from God.

In Christian theology God does *not* 'light the blue touch paper' and retire. No, God's creative activity is an ongoing process, not a single act at the beginning of time. The universe does not run itself autonomously but God sustains it in being continuously by his creative will and, if his will were withdrawn, the universe would cease to be.

From the many-worlds hypothesis and from quantum vacuum arguments, however, it is evident the proposition that God exists is not compelling in an absolute sense. And this too in a strange way is in accord with Christian belief, for God does not force us to believe in him. If there were some rational argument which could not be gainsaid, men would have no choice about whether to believe in God and offer him the honour which is his due. The Christian God is not like that. He wants us to come to him in penitence and faith and voluntarily offer him our worship and obedience.

We now need to examine, utilising the insights of modern science, how God might act in the world he has created.

How can God act in the world?

Verily thou art a God that hidest thyself, O God of Israel, the Saviour.

(Isaiah 45:15.)

We have seen that belief in God as designer and creator of the universe is quite rational in the light of modern science; indeed there are strong philosophical and scientific arguments in favour of such a belief. We must now consider the equally fundamental question — assuming that God exists, is he anything more than the Prime Mover, active at the initial creation only or does he, indeed can he, act in the world?

We saw in Chapters 2 and 3 that science has elucidated laws of nature which govern the behaviour of the universe and all its constituent parts. These laws seem to be universal in their application, and all matter obeys them. Nevertheless we have begun to see that there are limits to what we can know through science. At higher levels of organization, new emergent features come into play that were not predictable from lower level physical laws. The old clockwork image of the universe is dead.

The mechanistic view was inimical to the idea of God acting in the world — it seemed to leave no room for him to do so, for, as Laplace had seen, Newton's laws led inexorably to determinism.

In the light of these newer findings of science, of the Christian claim that God acts in the world, say in Biblical or secular history, or in response to prayer? Many regard the laws of nature as God-given, but deny a rôle for God beyond ordaining such laws and providing the initial conditions (thus they deny the *sustaining* rôle we described above). That is the deist, as opposed to the theist position. It is held by some in the Christian community, perhaps those who have not fully grasped the implications of recent trends in science. Thus Professor Maurice Wiles sees divine action 'in relation to the world as a whole rather than to particular occurrences within it',[35] and while, to be fair, he describes himself as a theist, it is in practice hard to distinguish his position from that of the deist.

Orthodox Christians believe, in contrast, that God acts in the world not only through his general providence, which can be seen in the orderly working out of the laws of nature, for example in the cycle of the returning seasons, but also through his special providence in the lives of individuals, and through miracle.

We have already seen (Chapter 6) John Polkinghorne's view of the universe as exhibiting emergent properties of flexibility and openness, and it is here that we may begin to see how God might act in unseen ways in his universe. Yes, order and general providence are built in through the laws and initial conditions (and chaos theory shows, as we have seen, that although we cannot predict in detail, there are broad properties of a system amenable to prediction). But God is also able to act within the system once it has got going. If an electron on the other side of the universe affects what gas particles in a box will be doing in 10^{-10} seconds, it is not difficult to imagine God providentially at work, moulding the system to his own purposes, responding to prayer, yet for these actions to be undetected and unamenable to scientific, experimental verification. Where events are probabilistic in nature a particular chain of events may have the appearance of being totally random (or not in any way departing from natural law), while in reality being guided by the divine will. As the writer of the book of Proverbs puts it (Proverbs 16:33):

> The lot is cast into the lap; but the whole disposing thereof is of the LORD.

I am not advocating the view that God manipulates every single quantum event. That way lies determinism again. Chance events would not really be chance events at all, but direct acts of God. This is the view of physicist turned theologian William Pollard,[36] and also of Donald MacKay,[37] and is open to the objection that the freedom of the world, including especially man's free will, is removed. Another, more technical objection, raised by David Bartholomew[38] to this view, is that true randomness is difficult to imitate in this way (even for God!) Suppose, for example, that I toss 1000 coins. It is not enough to make a sequence random that it has roughly the same number of heads as tails, but the order must also be random. Obviously 500 heads followed by 500 tails would not be random, but would require some other explanation. Departures from true randomness would in principle be detectable.

We tend to associate randomness with destructiveness, yet this connection is not a necessary one. We ourselves use randomness constructively, for example when we toss a coin to decide fairly which side starts a game. In card games, it is important to shuffle the pack to give variety as well as impose fairness. In computer simulations we use randomness to provide variety and unpredictability, important for example in testing the skills of a pilot. So God may be content to allow his creation to explore fruitful avenues through randomness.

In the universe as we find it chance is interwoven with law. Thus, in evolution, chance mutations are sifted through natural selection, and the result is increased complexity. There is no reason to suppose that the overall trend is not purposive, and working according to God's plan. Just as random tossing of coins leads to a proportion of heads closer and closer to 0.5 as the number of tosses increases (a non-random result), so the result of countless random events in nature converges to those far from random phenomena, conscious human beings who speculate on the meaning of it all. Computer scientists are now mimicking nature in utilising randomness in so-called 'genetic algorithms', which have applications in engineering, particularly robotics.

Rather than following Pollard into the intricacies of each atomic event, I am inclined to see God acting in an analogous way to humans. Our minds influence matter, as we have seen, by downward causation; this happens in any act of will, and without violating any laws of nature. Might not the mind of God similarly, yet far more powerfully, act on the matter of his created universe?

Process theology, the school arising out of the philosophy of A. N. Whitehead,[39] sees the action of God as 'a creative power of love behind and within the worldly process'.[38] God responds in love to the world in a manner that is persuasive rather than controlling.[39] There is much in this view, particularly in so far as it helps to mitigate the problems of suffering and evil (they are not so directly attributable to God). However, like the 'God's World, God's Body' idea which we discussed in the previous chapter, while being useful as a model it gives insufficient weight to God's transcendence, his separateness from creation. Indeed process theology takes us back to the Platonic idea of creation out of chaos, rather than the traditional doctrine of *creatio ex nihilo*.

I believe that it is perfectly possible to hold a view of the mind of God acting on the matter of the universe without sacrificing the vital notion of his transcendence. A picture I find particularly helpful is that given by J. R. Lucas:

> God's plan for the future must be like that of the Persian rugmakers, who let their children help them. In each family the children work at one end of the rug, the father at the other. The children fail to

carry out their father's instructions exactly, but so great is their father's skill, that he adapts his design at his end to take in each error at the children's end, and work it into a new, constantly adapted, pattern. So too, God.[42]

Lucas sees God as having not one, but infinitely many plans for the world, which he implements in response to the actions of the free agents, men, he has created. A similar idea has been expressed by Sir John Houghton, who sees God as the supreme chess grand master.[43] The outcome of the game is not in doubt, but the way that outcome is reached depends on the moves made both by the human and divine players.

With Bartholomew, I would see a prime locus for God's interaction with the world in that peak of creative complexity, the human mind. It is the mind (associated with but, as we have seen, not to be identified with the brain) which gives human beings their freedom — a true freedom, not determined, according to the modern scientific views which we have been discussing. Here especially God will be working his purpose out, particularly in response to the prayers of those who freely submit themselves to him, but also acting to oppose man where the purposes of man conflict with God's:

> If man is accepted as fellow labourer engaged in creative work, then a prime place for God's action would be at the springs of creative thought in the human mind.[44]

In the actions stemming from the unpredictability of the human mind, God will be at work,[45] but his influence in this way will not be absolute and will not therefore remove man's freedom, as would total manipulation of the sub-atomic world on Pollard's view.

On these considerations it will be seen that prayer is after all a rational activity. MacKay argues that even prayer for an outcome which is already determined at the time of prayer is rational.[46] He does so on the grounds that a universe in which the prayer had not been made would be an altogether different universe. Even if we have some doubts about the force of that argument, surely there can be little doubt that prayer can be efficacious when the outcome is open in the more flexible, non-predictable universe that current science is portraying. The Book of Common Prayer of the Church of England contains prayers for rain and fair weather, surely quite rational requests of God for which we can expect an answer, at any rate if they are not offered frivolously but for serious reasons, say in time of drought. It is gratifying to note that Sir John Houghton, Director General of the Meteorological Office, prays about the weather as he does about other things![47] Also prayers for individuals, say for healing, conversion and inner peace seem very reasonable in the light of the above.

Whether God does act in these ways is of course rather speculative, and it would be dangerous to dogmatize, yet it does seem consonant with the kind of world science is presenting to us. This is a world governed by natural law (these laws given and faithfully sustained by God), but also a world with a genuine openness, flexibility and freedom. Within that freedom lies man's own free-will as a conscious, rational being, and also God's freedom to fulfil his special providential care for man and the rest of creation.

Miracles

No testimony is sufficient to establish a miracle, unless the testimony be of such a kind, that its falsehood would be more miraculous than the fact which it endeavours to establish: and even in that case there is a mutual destruction of arguments, and the superior only gives us an assurance suitable to that degree of force which remains after deducting the inferior.

(David Hume, *On Miracles*.)

We have said that Christians see God acting in the world in three distinct ways, in general and special providence, as we have discussed above, and in miracle. We have seen that his acting providentially is quite compatible with the laws of nature as uncovered by science — none of these laws is broken. A moving example in

Scripture of God acting through special providence is given in the book of Ruth. The women Naomi and her daughter-in-law Ruth return to Judah after many years absence, bereaved and destitute. Ruth goes to glean ears of corn, following the Jewish law that the field is not harvested bare but an amount is left for the poor. It turns out, providentially, that the field where Ruth gleans belongs to her nearest kinsman Boaz, whose duty it is under Jewish law to take Ruth as his wife and raise up heirs on behalf of Ruth's dead husband. The security and future of Naomi and Ruth are thereby assured. And more important still is that God is working out his redemptive plan for mankind through these events in the lives of these simple folk, for the line of descent from Boaz and Ruth, passing through David, culminates in the birth of Christ.

There is nothing in the above account which would disconcert any scientist — no law of nature is broken: we simply have a happy concatenation of events. A scientist may miss the significance of these events if he approaches them in a reductionist frame of mind, but will not be unduly worried by them. Yet the Bible asserts that there is another class of events, seemingly more dramatic, which do seem to break the laws of nature: miracles. The parting of the Red Sea and the Resurrection of Christ are supreme examples.

Some philosophers, notably David Hume as quoted above, make categorical assertions that miracles cannot happen. Yet we have seen earlier, in Chapter 3, that scientific method is inductive rather than deductive (ironically, induction was criticized by Hume!). There is no reason in logic why, if a thousand times I observe an apple fall down from a tree, the one thousand and first time it should not fall up. We have seen that scientific theories according to Popper are always tentative, waiting for that thousand and first apple to falsify them. On the other hand we have seen that scientists in formulating their laws, and in the very fact of being able to do science, are relying on there being order and pattern in the universe. They see themselves gaining a 'tightening grasp of an actual reality' in Polkinghorne's useful phrase. The natural conclusion from all this is that miracles certainly cannot be ruled out, but that if they occur they will be very rare. That is just what orthodox Christians, at any rate, assert.

C. S. Lewis has succinctly countered Hume's argument. From the observed regularity of nature Hume concludes that there is 'uniform experience' against miracle. He thus concludes that miracles are the most improbable occurrences and that it is always more probable that the witness was lying or mistaken. But the argument is circular for, as Lewis says:

> Now of course we must agree with Hume that if there is absolutely "uniform experience" against miracles, if in other words they have never happened, why then they never have. Unfortunately we know the experience against them to be uniform only if we know that all the reports of them are false. And we can know all the reports to be false only if we know already that miracles have never occurred.[48]

Hume has his modern counterparts. In 1984 *The Times* published a letter from fourteen British professors of science, including six Fellows of the Royal Society, which supported belief in the gospel miracles. The prestigious scientific journal *Nature* published a leading article in response in which it defined miracles as 'inexplicable and irreproducible phenomena (which) do not occur'! Talk about begging the question! Fortunately the balance was redressed with a lucid attack on the reductionist position of the journal and a defence of complementary explanations of causation by Professor R J Berry, one of the fourteen.[49]

Miracles to the Christian are not arbitrary, magical occurrences; they are riven with meaning as one would expect of messages from God. The most important miracles centre round the person of Christ and if He is the unique Son of God it is perhaps not surprising that they should. Of course the central miracle, as C. S. Lewis points out,[50] is the Incarnation itself: that God became Man in Christ. We can see that many of the miracles Jesus performed are acted parables. The giving of sight to the blind symbolizes the spiritual enlightenment Christ brings, the feeding of the five thousand is a symbol of the spiritual food Christ offers in himself and so on.

We shall see in the next chapter that there is strong evidence for the resurrection, and that alternative explanations are highly implausible. The resurrection of Christ shows that death cannot contain the Son of God, it vindicates his defeat of sin on the cross, and it portends our own resurrection. And what I am suggesting here is that we can believe the evidence for it — science does not and indeed cannot, despite philosophers like Hume, deny the possibility of miracles.

There is a possible objection to all this which may be going through the minds of many readers. If God can act through providence and even more powerfully through miracle, why does he seemingly do so little — why does he allow so much suffering in the world? Here is not the place to do full justice to such a question but I shall attempt a few pointers by way of answer. These pointers lie in the character of God and in the nature of the world he has created. He has created a world with freedom and flexibility in it. The world is far more than a machine programmed to behave in a particular way. God's purpose is to create a world of maximal good and value and this necessarily has in it free, rational creatures who are not automatons. As Professor Keith Ward argues,[51] if these creatures are to be truly free, then they will be free in particular to disobey God, and to harm each other in pursuit of their own selfishness.

When God acts he respects his own creation. If he acts miraculously this is not because he has made a mistake in the laws of nature, but because he has a very special message to convey. But miracle is likely to coerce obedience rather than elicit it freely, so he will use miracle sparingly. He is however at work providentially, not a little, but all the time. He responds to prayer and he is at work unseen and often unperceived in the lives of his creatures. Although he is omnipotent, it is through the free cooperation, faith and prayer of his servants that he chooses to work. This is borne out by Jesus' restricted power in the face of unbelief: 'And he could there do no mighty work, save that he laid his hands upon a few sick folk and healed them' (Mark 6:5).

The final answer to the problem of suffering must lie in the cross. Here God shared the suffering of the world, and took it upon himself. Jesus, the innocent victim, suffered one of the most brutal judicial punishments ever devised by man. He was deserted by his friends and he witnessed the agony of his mother at the foot of the cross. Above all, and this is a mystery of which we can never plumb the depths, in 'becoming sin' for us, he who 'knew no sin' endured the ultimate pain of separation from his heavenly Father, the one who in holiness and purity could not look on sin.

But these thoughts move us on to new ground. We may have established that theism is all very well and respectable, but is the Christian story, with its audaciously specific claims, credible in the age of science? This is the question I now address.

CHAPTER 10

The Christian Story

> And is it true? And is it true,
> This most tremendous tale of all,
> Seen in a stained-glass window's hue,
> A Baby in an ox's stall?
> The Maker of the stars and sea
> Become a Child on earth for me?
>
> (Sir John Betjeman, *Christmas*.)

In the previous chapter we saw that science, in particular the new physics, is much more consonant with the presence and action of God in the universe than the old mechanistic model. Of course we have to be a little bit careful about such claims, because scientific theories are somewhat ephemeral, and those we have today are likely to be superseded in the future. Nevertheless we have seen some fundamental objections to the idea that we can find a wholly deterministic and predictive theory, which embraces the universe and mind in particular.

There are strong arguments in favour of theism, but can we particularize and argue in favour of Christianity?

In this chapter I present a very brief overview of just what Christian belief entails, and then proceed to show that this belief is indeed founded upon good evidence. Just as the human mind cannot be reduced to neurophysiological impulses in the brain and so ultimately to particle physics, so too theology cannot be reduced to psychology and the lower level sciences. So the evidence adduced in this chapter will generally be of a different kind from that considered in the bulk of this book: historical and experiential rather than physical and experimental, though natural science will again play a part.

The basic components of Christian belief are: creation, fall, redemption, incarnation, resurrection. These are grand themes indeed to which it is impossible to do justice here. A few sentences on each will have to suffice just to set the scene for what I want to say in the bulk of the chapter about evidence.

First, it is fundamental to Christian faith that God is creator. We have already seen how the Christian doctrine of creation is concerned with ontological rather than temporal origin, how it embraces God's sustaining of the universe, and how the traditional cosmological and design arguments still apply.

The Bible opens in Genesis Chapter 1 with the majestic sweep of creation: 'In the beginning God created the heaven and the earth'. There is no more sublime description than this and our scientific accounts are ponderous and banal in comparison with the poetry and simplicity of Genesis.

We have seen how Genesis Chapter 1 is not intended to give scientific information. Rather it tells us that all things are created by God and that man is the pinnacle of creation: 'So God created man in his own image, in the image of God created he him; male and female created he them' (Gen 1:27). All the rest of creation is made for man's benefit: the sun and moon set in the firmament 'to give light upon the earth'; 'the fish of the sea, the fowl of the air and every living thing that moveth upon the earth', over which man is to have dominion; and the herbs and trees, which are to provide him with food. God has made man in his own image as the steward of His creation. Furthermore God was pleased with his creation: it was good.

This is the basic assumption of the Bible; it is not argued for, but assumed as the starting point of all that follows. That God exists and made the world is, if you like, the Bible's axiom, the premise on which all else hangs. Of course the Biblical writers are well aware that the creation is a stupendous advertisement for the creator: 'The heavens declare the glory of God: and the firmament sheweth his handywork' (Psalm 19:1). But perhaps in one or two places only is the self-evident truth of this axiom argued for, as it were in debate. In Acts 14:17 St Paul rebukes the Lycaonians for offering Barnabas and himself the worship due to God alone. As evidence for God's activity he states:

> Nevertheless, he left not himself without witness, in that he did good, and gave us rain from heaven, and fruitful seasons, filling our hearts with food and gladness.

Further, in Romans 1:20 St Paul affirms that humans are without excuse in denying God, for 'the invisible things of him from the creation of the world are clearly seen, being understood by the things that are made, even his eternal power and Godhead'. And this brings us on to that very thing, man's denial of God.

The fundamental message of the Garden of Eden story is that man is in a state of rebellion against his creator. In theological terms he is a 'fallen' creature. God wants for man the very best. That he has made him in his own image means that man, uniquely amongst creation, can have a relationship with God. Yet the consciousness, freedom and autonomy which God has bestowed on man have been abused by him. He has gone his own, selfish way. He has turned away from God, and he has turned away from his fellow men, whom he is commanded to love. As we read in the book of Isaiah (Isaiah 53:6):

> All we like sheep have gone astray; we have turned every one to his own way.

We have seen how modern evolutionary theory and depth psychology are in accord with the Biblical view of man as sinful. He has through his genetic make-up sinful desires, but he also possesses the freewill to yield to them or deny them.

We in the twentieth century hardly need reminding of man's corruption and 'inhumanity'. From the concentration camps of Nazi Germany to 'ethnic cleansing' in Bosnia, we are starkly reminded that, far from 'having come of age', man is fundamentally flawed. While he is capable of great good and noble sacrifice, a realistic assessment must also take account of the dark side of human nature, which we all share.

All is far from lost, however. God still loves mankind and has set in motion his plan of redemption, the history of which is documented in Scripture. God has chosen a particular people, the Jews, through whom he brings about the redemption of all mankind. The Exodus from Egyptian slavery and entry into the promised land, which Israel continually looks back to, are a model and a foreshadowing of the redemption of man from sin and God's gift to him of the Saviour and an eternal home in heaven. His covenant with Israel, in which God's law is given on tablets of stone, is a model and a foreshadowing of the New Covenant or Testament later brought about by Christ, in which God's laws are written in men's hearts (Jeremiah 31:33).

In the Old Testament God chooses certain individuals — Abraham, Moses, the prophets — who have a special relationship with him and who are to be ministers of his covenant.

The sacrificial system inaugurated in the Old Testament teaches that man's sin must be atoned for. God is righteous and cannot look on sin (Habakkuk 1:13). The whole ritual of purification, of the priest entering the sanctuary once a year, behind the veil, on the Day of Atonement, and of the offering of sacrifices, shows the separation that man's sin has wrought between him and God. The animal sacrifices of the Old Testament foreshadow the one, true and perfect sacrifice for sins made by Jesus on the Cross.

For in the fulness of time God sent his only Son to take on human flesh, and to die for us, in our place. As we have seen, C. S. Lewis regarded the incarnation as the greatest miracle. In the words of Charles Wesley, it reveals:

> Our God contracted to a span,
> Incomprehensibly made man.

The Incarnation thus signifies God become man, sharing our very nature, our joys and sorrows, and ultimately suffering betrayal, desertion by his closest friends, and an unspeakably brutal death. In particular, following our earlier discussion, it signifies the sanctification of the material world. As that great hymn of the church, the *Te Deum*, so graphically puts it: 'When thou tookest upon thee to deliver man: thou didst not abhor the Virgin's womb.' Again we see the balance in Christian thought, in contrast to Greek thought or Eastern mysticism: nature is the good creation of God, fit even for him to enter in human form.

Now Christ's death was for a purpose, the sacrifice for sins which the animal offerings could not achieve (Heb 10:4). St Anselm of Canterbury recognised that only God himself *could* in fact make the necessary reparation for sin. Man cannot contribute anything, for he owes his very all to God in the first place.[1] Yet only man *should* make reparation, 'otherwise man does not make amends'.[2] This leads to the only possibility for man's salvation: that one who is perfect God and perfect man should make the necessary satisfaction,[3] and Jesus Christ the Son of God is just such.

This salvation wrought for man is appropriated by him in taking the step of faith and making an act of commitment to Christ, always remembering that it is God's grace and not his own merit which has brought this about (Eph 2:8,9). The Holy Spirit, the third person of the Triune God in whom Christians believe, the first two being the Father and the Son, comes to dwell within the new believer. By the Spirit's aid the Christian is slowly transformed into the likeness of Christ and assisted in his earthly pilgrimage. He develops his relationship with God through prayer, meditation on God's word in Scripture, and through partaking in the corporate life of the church, especially the sacraments.

If Christ's death achieves the forgiveness of man's sin and his reconciliation to God, it is the resurrection of Christ which vindicates his sacrifice — because God did not let Jesus rot in a tomb but raised him up, and exalted him to his right hand on high. We have seen the importance for Christian thought that Christ was raised *bodily.*

Very importantly, it is the resurrection of Christ which guarantees us our own eternal life. Jesus is the 'firstfruits of them that slept', and in the end, death itself, the last enemy, shall be destroyed (1 Cor 15:26). We, too, shall be raised 'incorruptible' and united with Christ in his eternal kingdom.

This, then, is the Christian story. In many ways, for example in language and imagery, it seems far removed from the kind of discussion we have been having to date. We must now examine if and how such a picture can be reconciled with a modern scientific outlook on the world.

Scientific tools applied to the Christian faith

The religion that is afraid of science dishonours God and commits suicide.

(Ralph Waldo Emerson, *Journals* [1831].)

In *The Selfish Gene*, Richard Dawkins makes a particularly vitriolic attack on religion. To Dawkins faith means 'blind trust, in the absence of evidence, even in the teeth of evidence'.[4] He goes on to discuss the story of doubting Thomas, saying that the story is told, not that we should admire Thomas, but so that we should admire the other apostles in comparison. However, Thomas demanded evidence whereas the others did not, so in Dawkins's view 'Thomas is the only really admirable member of the twelve apostles'.[5] It is in any case a bizarre piece of Biblical exegesis, completely missing the point that the other apostles had already had the evidence of meeting the risen Christ in person when Thomas was absent. But, more importantly, is the basic thesis of Dawkins true, that religious faith is not only lacking in evidence, but 'explicitly eschews evidence'?

I think we can already answer no to this. The very existence of the world and the order within it comprise powerful evidence for the existence of God. Yet much of our earlier discussion might seem to convey only a rather negative message: the Biblical doctrine of creation is not contradicted by science (as we saw in Chapter 4), and the nature of the world as revealed by science certainly leaves room for God to exist and to act (Chapter 9). But does he indeed act, and if so, how has he acted? Is there evidence to support the Christian belief system presented in the first part of this chapter?

Let us turn to positive evidence in favour of the Christian faith, for notwithstanding Dawkins there is in fact plenty! In particular we look scientifically at the evidence both that God has acted historically in Biblical history and in the life, death and resurrection of Christ, and is active today in the lives of many people.

We shall not be able to prove incontrovertibly that Christianity is true by such an approach. We have seen in Chapter 3 that science itself is unable to prove any of its statements. But we shall present evidence for which the Christian position seems the most reasonable to adopt, and along the way see how some other rival theories have been falsified. We start with the documentary evidence.

The authenticity of the documents

If the Bible is not the true religion, one is very excusable in being deceived, for everything in it is grand and worthy of God. The more I consider the Gospel, the more I am assured there is nothing there which is not beyond the march of events and above the human mind.

(Napoleon Bonaparte.)

Christianity is the religion of a book. Much therefore depends on the integrity of the book. In this and the next section we discuss the reliability of the Bible and how it has been studied from a scientific point of view.

The rise of scientific study of the Bible really began in Germany, particularly at the University of Tübingen, in the late eighteenth and early nineteenth centuries. Until then no one had thought to study the Biblical writings as they would any other book. Since then, the development of Biblical criticism has been so prolific that now no book has been nearly so dissected and analysed as has the Bible.

What are the tools used by scholars to study the Bible scientifically? I shall give a brief résumé of the main techniques and the results obtained from them, and I shall concentrate on the New Testament, mainly because that contains the foundational documents of Christianity but also because the Old Testament would deserve a tome in its own right.

The use of the adjective 'scientific' to describe the methods of historical and literary enquiry may be unfamiliar to some readers. John Robinson[6] recounts the story of a modern university only becoming convinced that theology was a science when its first professor in the subject, a textual critic, began by ordering a supply of photographic equipment and then applied for a building in which to house it! But the term is appropriate to describe the systematic, analytical approach of modern scholars. Just as in the natural sciences we find hypotheses being put forward and tested against the evidence, so we see the same processes at work in Biblical scholarship. We see the falsification of theories and the substitution of new ones, and, despite many current controversies, theologians too can be said to be gaining a 'tightening grasp of an actual reality', to use Polkinghorne's expression once more.

We have indeed come a long way from the early scepticism of the Tübingen school, which placed composition of the New Testament a couple of hundred years after the events portrayed, and, while naïve views of divine dictation are also no longer tenable, we have arrived at a picture of these documents as remarkably well attested and reliable.

Biblical criticism

I must confess to you that the majesty of the Scriptures astonished me; the holiness of the Evangelists speaks to my heart and has such striking characters of truth, and is, moreover, so perfectly inimitable, that if it had been the invention of men, the inventors would be greater than the greatest heroes.

(Jean-Jacques Rousseau.)

The first point to establish in approaching the New Testament writings is the text itself. Over the centuries of the Christian era many, many copies have been made, with the inevitable introduction of errors, however painstaking the copying process may have been. The purpose of the science of *textual criticism* is to trace the family trees of the many thousands of extant manuscripts in order to get back as close as possible to what the original authors wrote. It involves the careful weighing of evidence — which of these two alternative readings is more likely to be original? Is this simply a copying error or has the scribe deliberately altered something he himself finds unpalatable?

Following the pioneering work of F. J. A. Hort in the nineteenth century, textual critics have devised rules to apply in such circumstances. Examples include taking the shorter of variant readings of a sentence or passage on the grounds that it is more usual to add embellishments than to subtract material, and taking the more difficult reading on the grounds that it is natural for scribes to amend in the direction hard-to-easy, rather than the other way round. Often, however, it is a matter of fine judgment which text to take when ambiguity is present.

Just as important, if not more so, as using extant manuscripts of the New Testament itself in this work is the use of other early documents which quote the New Testament, since these can often take us further back in time still. It so happens that most of our New Testament is quoted by the early church fathers. Virtually the whole of it is quoted for example in Irenaeus writing in about 180 AD Quotations are also found in much earlier documents, for example the Epistle of Clement to the Corinthians (dated about AD 96), the Epistles of Ignatius (the latest of which, to the Romans, was written on the author's journey to martyrdom in Rome in AD 115), and the collection of teachings known as the *Didache*.

It was with these immediate successors to the New Testament that the great nineteenth century English Biblical scholar, J. B. Lightfoot, Hulsean Professor of Divinity and Fellow of Trinity College, Cambridge, began his work in dating the New Testament. He was thus able to refute (falsify, to use Popper's word) the wild claims of very late authorship coming out of the German school.[7] For, clearly, not only do these quotations of the New Testament help us in getting back to the original text, but, since we know *their* dates (admittedly after considerable detective work on their authenticity), they put stringent limits on the dates of authorship of the New Testament itself.

The results of the detective work of textual criticism are truly astonishing. The New Testament is in fact vastly better attested than any other body of literature from the ancient world. For example, for Caesar's *Gallic War*, composed between 58 and 50 BC there are only about 9 or 10 at all decent manuscripts, and the oldest dates from 900 years after the work's composition. The earliest manuscripts of the Greek historians Thucydides and Herodotus date from some 1,300 years after their composition. The list goes on — for Aeschylus we have a single late manuscript and for Catullus only copies of a single, now lost, fifteenth century manuscript. To take a scientific example, Euclid's *Elements* was written, or compiled and edited, in about 300 BC, yet the earliest extant manuscripts are Byzantine and date from the 10th century. Of course no one doubts the authenticity of any of these works!

In contrast, however, there are several thousand copies of the Greek New Testament of importance for establishing the text. Amongst the most important are the Codex Vaticanus, held in the Vatican, and the Codex Sinaiaticus, held in the British Museum, both dating from the mid fourth century. There are hundreds of other witnesses from within three hundred years of the New Testament's composition, including a fragment of John's gospel dated palaeographically at about AD 130, a mere 30-40 years from its generally agreed composition.

Moreover, as can be judged by looking at the marginal notes of variant readings in a modern translation such as the Revised Standard Version, it can be safely concluded that doubts about the actual text are so small as to affect no aspect of Christian faith or practice.

Another technique used by Biblical scholars, *source criticism*, has the aim of getting from the text back a further stage, to the date of composition, the author's identity and the literary sources used in composition. A reading of, say, the first three gospels will reveal that they are clearly related: they have much material in common although the same stories are often repeated with variation. By placing these gospels side by side we can glean several facts, from which some natural conclusions can be drawn. First, virtually the whole of Mark is repeated in Matthew and Luke. Secondly, there is a further body of material, largely sayings of Jesus, which Matthew and Luke have in common, but which are not found in Mark. Thirdly, each of Matthew and Luke has a certain amount of material unique to himself. Careful study of the ordering of events in these three gospels, and the variations in accounts of the same events, has led to the consensus of scholarly opinion that Mark is the first of the gospels to be written, and that, in addition to Mark, Matthew and Luke had a written collection of Jesus' sayings known as 'Q' to hand when they were writing ('Q' stands for the German word *Quelle* meaning 'source'). Mark is generally put at being written in about 65 AD with Matthew and Luke at about 80-90 AD. Through 'Q', however, we may well be getting back to material written down for church instruction as early as 50 AD.

It is possible to attempt to go back even further to the oral 'forms' or patterns in which the original preaching and teaching of Jesus and the apostles were given, ie even before the circulation of such written material from which the gospels were composed. This is the concern of another technique, known as *form criticism*. This technique is also vitally concerned with the importance to the life of the church community of this oral material and the influence of this on the 'form' in which it was passed on. By taking account of the ways in which the church may have used or modified the tradition we have a further means of getting back to the precise teaching of Jesus himself. However, form criticism is less exact than the other techniques so far discussed and in practice has probably speculated too much on the problems facing the early church in which Jesus' teaching may have been remembered or passed on.

An interesting point that arises from *linguistic* study stems from the fact that, although the New Testament is written entirely in Greek, the *lingua franca* of the day, Jesus and his Jewish followers actually spoke Aramaic, sister language to Hebrew in which the Old Testament is written. If we translate Jesus' sayings back into Aramaic we find that many of them are poetic in form, exhibiting parallelism, poetical rhythm and even, occasionally, rhyme.[8] Such features are common to the Hebrew prophets of the Old Testament, and would have made Jesus' words especially memorable to his followers, as no doubt they were designed to do. Here is thus a further strand to the confidence we can place in the authenticity of the New Testament.

The conclusion put forward by F. F. Bruce is that none of the critical methods applied to the Bible ever lead to a non-supernatural Jesus.[9]

Just as in the natural sciences theories come and go, so do they in Biblical scholarship, though, as we have indicated, Biblical scholars, like scientists, believe they are making genuine progress. As an example of the questioning of established theories we can cite the views of the late John Robinson, former Bishop of Woolwich and Dean of Trinity College, Cambridge, and one of the most eminent of modern British Biblical scholars, on John's gospel. Until recently John has been regarded as of late composition (c. 90-100 AD) and as giving more the church's reflection on Christ than straight history. It does clearly differ in style and content from the other three so called 'synoptic' gospels. However, Robinson wants to place it as the first gospel to be composed, and therefore to be much more historically reliable than had been thought heretofore.[10] In fact he dates the whole of the New Testament before 70 AD on the grounds that no mention is made of the destruction of Jerusalem by the Romans under Titus in that year as a past event.[11] While Robinson's views are not widely shared by New Testament scholars, it is rather remarkable that someone of such stature can put forward a plausible case for much earlier dates than the already very early, prevailing consensus.

The gospel miracles

If the ultimate Fact is not an abstraction but the living God, opaque by the very fulness of His blinding actuality, then He might do things. He might work miracles.

(C. S. Lewis.[12])

We have seen in the previous chapter that miracles cannot be ruled out by modern science. We argued that the New Testament miracles centring on the person of Christ were not magical tricks but expressed messages from God and were in character with the kind of God in which Christians believe. We have now surveyed the evidence for the authenticity of the New Testament writings. It is clear that miracles form an early part of the gospel tradition. As with all this tradition we shall want to judge critically, taking each account on its merits. However, no matter how many skins of the onion we peel away from the gospel accounts, we simply cannot get back to a purely human Jesus. Of course the kind of scientific-historical methods of research that we have been discussing cannot prove that the miracles occurred — we have seen time and again that no science 'proves' anything in the strict sense. But this approach might have been expected to 'rumble' them if they were untrue, merely late accretions imposed by a second or third century church upon its founder (incidentally there do exist late 'apocryphal' gospels with clearly legendary material of this kind).

One approach to the gospel miracles is to attempt to rationalize them. For example, when Jesus fed the five thousand, what really happened was that his hearers heard his message of love for others and were moved to bring out of their pockets the food they actually had on them and to share it. Or, when Jesus turned the water into wine at the wedding feast in Cana of Galilee he was merely indulging in a playful joke in which the master of the feast and the guests joined in. Such interpretations completely fail to do justice to the text as we have it. The stories were included precisely because they were miraculous. The miracles of Jesus in the gospels are referred to by the gospel writers as 'signs and wonders' because they were recognised to be out of the ordinary. First century Jews did not need the formulations of Newtonian mechanics in order to know the difference between the ordinary, everyday and something which had invaded nature from outside.

When we come to the resurrection of Christ, as with much of the New Testament material we find varying accounts in the four gospels. It may be argued that certain elements of these accounts have a legendary feel to them, such as the episode of the saints rising from their tombs and appearing to many, given only in Matthew's gospel. However, at the end of the day, we are left with a common core of material. The tomb was empty; Jesus appeared after his death both to individuals and to groups; and the Jewish authorities could not disprove the disciples' claim. Perhaps the best attestation comes not in the gospels at all, but in St Paul's first epistle to the Corinthians, where the apostle claims to be handing on the tradition which he had himself received (1 Cor 15:3,4):

> For I delivered unto you first of all that which I also received, how that Christ died for our sins according to the scriptures; and that he was buried, and that he rose again the third day according to the scriptures: and that he was seen of Cephas [Peter], then of the twelve: After that he was seen of above five hundred brethren at once; of whom the greater part remain unto this present, but some are fallen asleep.

This witness is particularly valuable since it is earlier than the gospels themselves, being written about 54 AD Paul goes on to say in this passage how fundamental the doctrine of the resurrection is to the Christian faith: our own resurrection depends on it and, if it is not true, we are 'of all men most miserable' (1 Cor 15:19).

Again, people have tried to put forward alternative hypotheses to explain away the resurrection. A temporary resuscitation does not do justice to the brutality of crucifixion. No one undergoing such an ordeal could persuade his followers that he were risen from the dead. Also the accounts make clear that Jesus was dead when he came down from the cross.

The idea that the disciples stole the body also bears no credence. These men proclaimed the resurrection from the housetops and many of them died for their belief — surely someone would have cracked under pressure if it were an elaborate hoax. Again, mass hallucination is hard to sustain considering the number of different appearances and the fact that, immediately following Jesus' death, his disciples were disillusioned and skulked away into hiding for fear of the authorities.

The only hypothesis which fits the evidence, and which has stood the test of time, is that Jesus truly rose from the dead.

The evidence from archaeology

> And as he went out of the temple, one of his disciples saith unto him, Master, see what manner of stones and buildings are here! and Jesus answering said unto him, Seest thou these great buildings? there shall not be left one stone upon another, that shall not be thrown down.
>
> (Mark 13:1,2.)

Evidence from archaeological digs at sites mentioned in the New Testament also provides corroboration for many of the Biblical narratives. For example, in John Chapter 5 Jesus is described as healing a paralytic at a pool, 'which is called in the Hebrew tongue Bethesda, having five porches' (John 5:2). Excavation in Jerusalem has uncovered a pool with precisely five porticoes, which archaeologists believe to be the pool of Bethesda. Interestingly, as we have seen, and notwithstanding John Robinson, the consensus among Biblical scholars is still that John is of later composition than the synoptic gospels and is more representative of the church's reflection on the life of Christ than historical. Thus, until this discovery, sceptical Biblical scholars had tended to interpret the five porticoes allegorically as representing the five books of the law of Moses. This clearly illustrates the current trend towards seeing John as more historical than heretofore.

A fascinating study of inscriptions (engravings on stone found all over the ancient world) by Sir William Ramsay towards the end of the nineteenth century has thrown remarkable light on the accuracy of St Luke, the author of Acts as well as the gospel attributed to him, as an historian.[13] Time and again Luke refers to the Roman officials of the various provinces of the Empire: Gallio, the proconsul of Achaia, but strategoi in Philippi, asiarchs in Ephesus, politarchs in Thessalonica, and so on. What Ramsay showed was that invariably Luke got the titles of these officials right. The feat has been compared with getting the titles of Heads of Colleges right in Oxford: the Dean of Christ Church, the Provost of Oriel, the Warden of Keble, the Master of Balliol and so on. Only an insider could possibly be expected not to trip up on such niceties. If Luke can be relied upon in matters of such detail, surely he can be relied on in the weightier matter of his narrative.

One of the most spectacular discoveries of all time for Biblical scholarship was made in 1947 when a Bedouin shepherd boy stumbled by accident into a cave at Qumran near the Dead Sea. A whole library of papyrus documents dating from the first century BC and the first century AD, and belonging to an ascetic Jewish sect (the Essenes), had been preserved in pots discovered in this and, subsequently, other caves. The finding of what we now know as the 'Dead Sea scrolls' was of the greatest possible relevance to the Old Testament since it gave manuscripts from all books of the Hebrew Bible, except for the book of Esther, pre-dating other Old Testament manuscripts by 900 to 1000 years. The Qumran text of the Old Testament confirms the remarkable accuracy of the traditional 10th century AD Massoretic text which had constituted the Hebrew Bible until the present day.

A similar treasure trove of papyri had been found in rubbish heaps at Oxyrhynchus in Egypt in 1897. All kinds of material shedding light on the language of the New Testament and including some hitherto unknown 'sayings of Jesus' were found here.

Far from undermining the Christian faith, time and again archaeology has assisted in aiding our understanding of the Bible and providing invaluable insight.

The natural sciences

There are more sure marks of authenticity in the Bible than in any profane history.

(Sir Isaac Newton.)

I have concentrated above on the specialist tools of Biblical scholarship, but the natural sciences have a part to play too. Generally scientists approaching the Bible have been less sceptical than theologians, preferring to take the texts at face value. Thus, astrophysicist Dr Graham Waddington of Oxford University and Dr Colin Humphreys, Professor of Materials Science at Cambridge University, using astronomical data on lunar eclipses and comparing with the Biblical descriptions, have recently pin-pointed the crucifixion to Friday, 3rd April, 33 AD.[14] 30 and 33 AD had been the most popular years among Biblical scholars with the former preferred.

To date the crucifixion involves determining in which of the possible years the Jewish date of 14th Nisan indicated by the Biblical records fell on a Friday. The first day of the month is counted from the new moon and can therefore be determined astronomically and correlated with the Julian calendar, and the 14th day calculated very simply from that. Humphreys and Waddington made the leap of identifying references to the moon being 'turned to blood' at the crucifixion (Acts 2:20) with a lunar eclipse which occurred on 3rd April 33 AD. This was the only eclipse in the period 26-36 AD which would have been visible from Jerusalem.

Interestingly, as noted in Chapter 4, Newton himself examined the same question. Using the same methods as Humphreys and Waddington he gave 3rd April 33 AD as his second choice, unfortunately plumping for his first choice of April 23rd 34 AD on the very tenuous grounds that the ripeness of the corn at Passover two years earlier (Luke 6:1) fitted well with a late Passover in 32 AD but not 31 AD.[15]

Astrophysicists have also been concerned to date Christ's birth by identifying the star of Bethlehem with known astronomical events such as planetary conjunctions or novae (which appear temporarily as very bright objects). The most popular explanation has been the conjunction of Jupiter and Saturn in 7 BC but in 1977 the nova theory resurfaced in a paper in *Quarterly Journal of the Royal Astronomical Society*.[16]

More recently, Colin Humphreys has examined this topic too.[17] He argues very plausibly for identifying the star with a comet, since this best fits with the Biblical description that the star 'went before them, till it came and stood over where the young child was' (Matthew 2:9). Chinese astronomers recorded a comet in the year 5 BC which was visible for 70 days between March 9th and May 4th. Humphreys argues from there being no room at the inn that Christ was most likely born at Passover between 13th and 27th April and that the Magi visited between 24th May and 8th June. No doubt the Magi had seen the conjunction of Jupiter and Saturn in 7 BC and the massing of Saturn, Jupiter and Mars in 6 BC, which set the scene for the birth of a mighty king to the Jews; and this was confirmed by the third powerful sign, the spectacular comet of 5 BC, which sent them on their journey.

Even so, Bulmer-Thomas[18] has argued, on the grounds that the gospel account does not specifically state that the star was in any way spectacular, that it was none of these signs which did the trick. Rather, the ordinary 'stopping' of the planet Jupiter in its journey across the sky is what finally sent the Magi going. Because both Jupiter and Earth are orbiting the sun, from earth we observe Jupiter first moving east to west against the stellar background, then slowing to a stationary point, before moving in retrograde motion east to west, coming to a second stationary point and starting the cycle again. I remain unconvinced by this last possibility (despite Bulmer-Thomas's arguments, it is just too ordinary!), preferring the highly plausible account of Humphreys.

In any case, for both the crucifixion and nativity we can see how the astronomers are able, in principle, further to refine dates already considerably narrowed by Biblical scholars.

Another scientific technique which has been applied in the Biblical sphere is radio carbon dating. This technique has recently been applied to the Dead Sea scrolls and confirms the 200 BC to 100 AD date previously obtained palaeographically. The technique has also been used to falsify the claim that the Turin shroud was the burial wrapping of Christ — the shroud was dated as of mediaeval origin.

Religious experience

Religious experience occurs in the sanctuary but its claim to truth has to be tested in the public world of facts where scientific disciplines operate.

(Lesslie Newbigin.[19])

The scientific study of religious experience really began in the late nineteenth and early twentieth century with the work of William James (brother of Henry, the novelist) and others of the New England school. James's book *The Varieties of Religious Experience* is a classic and deals particularly with the psychological aspects of religious experience, drawing on and analysing many examples. The book is based on the Gifford Lectures on Natural Religion which James was invited to give at Edinburgh University in 1901-1902.[20]

More recently much important work in this field has been carried out by the Alister Hardy Research Centre at Manchester College, Oxford. Sir Alister Hardy was an eminent marine biologist, a scientist of the first rank — Professor of Zoology at Oxford, Fellow of the Royal Society and scientific medallist of the Zoological Society. As a zoologist, like Dawkins, he was immersed in Darwinian theory. Yet from his youth, when he first experienced God himself in lone zoological and botanical walks in the Northamptonshire countryside, he had a burning ambition to apply scientific methods to the study of religion. After a glittering career as a conventional scientist his ambition was fulfilled when he was invited to set up the Religious Experience Research Unit, subsequently renamed the Alister Hardy Research Centre, at Manchester College.

Over the years the Alister Hardy Research Centre has amassed an enormous amount of data on religious experience, particularly in Britain, though similar work has been undertaken in the U.S.A. and Australia. A very readable account is given by David Hay (*Religious Experience Today*)[21] and indeed in Hardy's own seminal book *The Spiritual Nature of Man.*[22] The findings are truly startling. Far from being non-existent or confined to a few cranks, religious experience is widespread. Indeed between a third and a half of the adult population of Britain, according to the various national surveys carried out, believe they have had such an experience at least once in their lives. The figure rises to nearly two thirds if one takes the local studies done in Nottingham by Hay, where the interviewing techniques were more personal and relaxed than those of the national opinion polling organisations.

So what is the nature of these experiences and how do we go about analysing them?

Although the experiences are very varied, a taxonomy can be constructed just as in the study of biological species, which, you will remember, led Darwin to the breakthrough of the evolutionary understanding. Two main types of experience are generally identified in describing religious experience, the so-called 'numinous' and 'mystical'.

The term 'numinous' was coined by Professor Rudolph Otto in his book *Das Heilige.*[23] It describes an overwhelming experience of the presence of God, God as completely 'other', holy and awesome. Mystical experiences are characterized by a feeling of 'oneness' with nature.

The Alister Hardy Research Centre recognises these two major traditional categories, though it prefers an eight-fold classification, in which some of the categories either do not fit easily into the numinous or mystical or span both[24]:

Meaningful patterning of events
Awareness of the presence of God
Awareness of receiving help in prayer
Awareness of guiding presence not called God
Awareness of the presence of the dead

Awareness of a sacred presence in nature
Awareness of an evil presence
Experiencing that all things are 'One'

The following are two of the many examples cited by Hay and are typical of the experiences gleaned by the Hardy Centre.
The first comes from North Wales:

> I was a solitary person — not from choice — and I suppose I was lonely. But in the mountains I felt security and joy and a oneness with nature. One day, as I stood on a hill above our village, a clear bright windy day with a breeze rustling the dry heather, it seemed to me that I heard a voice quite distinctly calling me by name. Looking round and seeing no-one I felt suddenly foolish and laughed rather nervously. Then I heard the voice again: '———, follow me'. That was all ... no thunder and lightning — simply the wind rustling the heather. I lay down flat on my face and said quite simply 'Lord, I will follow'. As I said, I saw nothing. But a feeling of awe and a presence passing over me caused me to be there for some time, afraid to open my eyes.[25]

The second example describes a moment of panic for someone ill in hospital:

> ... the injections were very painful. I dreaded these more than anything. Then the sister came and patted my hand and told me a blood transfusion was to be set up. I fell into a complete, utter and absolute panic. I should scream and no-one screams in hospital— panic mounted. What should I do? I did not think to pray. Then Jesus stood by my ordinary hospital ward bed. It seemed quite natural. He was calm and serene and his whole presence filled me – his calmness and sereneness had a tremendous sense of power and love.[26]

This kind of experience is commonly described in Scripture and elsewhere in Christian literature. Jacob's wrestling with a nameless man (God?) is of this kind (Gen 32:24-30). Moses met with God at the burning bush (Ex 3:2ff) and on Mount Sinai (Ex 19:3). In Isaiah Chapter 6 we read of the prophet's majestic vision of the Lord's glory:

In the year that king Uzziah died I saw also the Lord sitting upon a throne, high and lifted up, and his train filled the temple. Above it stood the seraphims: each one had six wings; with twain he covered his face, and with twain he covered his feet, and with twain he did fly. And one cried unto another, and said, Holy, holy, holy, is the LORD of hosts: the whole earth is full of his glory. And the posts of the door moved at the voice of him that cried, and the house was filled with smoke. Then said I, Woe is me! for I am undone; because I am a man of unclean lips, and I dwell in the midst of a people of unclean lips: for mine eyes have seen the King, the LORD of hosts. Then flew one of the seraphims unto me, having a live coal in his hand, which he had taken with the tongs from off the altar: And he laid it upon my mouth, and said, Lo, this hath touched thy lips; and thine iniquity is taken away, and thy sin is purged. Also I heard the voice of the Lord, saying, Whom shall I send, and who will go for us? Then said I, Here am I; send me.

One is reminded too of St Paul's conversion on the Damascus road (Acts 9:3-6):

And as he journeyed, he came near Damascus: and suddenly there shined round about him a light from heaven: And he fell to the earth, and heard a voice saying unto him, Saul, Saul, why persecutest thou me? And he said, Who art thou, Lord? And the Lord said, I am Jesus whom thou persecutest: it is hard for thee to kick against the pricks. And he trembling and astonished said, Lord what wilt thou have me to do? And the Lord said unto him, Arise, and go into the city, and it shall be told thee what thou must do.

Such direct experiences of the presence of God, or of Christ, have been recorded down the ages by Christian saints. Perhaps those examples recorded in Scripture and in the great spiritual classics are more vivid and dramatic than those contemporary ones we have been examining, but that is not surprising since we are there in the realm of those who are acknowledged leaders in the spiritual realm. One Christian writer today who has given a vivid description of his own experience is Metropolitan Anthony Bloom. Bloom was an unbeliever, but had been angered by listening to a priest and decided to find out for himself about Christianity by reading the shortest of the gospels:

> While I was reading the beginning of St. Mark's Gospel, before I reached the third chapter, I suddenly became aware that on the other side of my desk there was a presence. And the certainty was so strong that it was Christ standing there that it has never left me. This was the real turning point. Because Christ was alive and I had been in his presence I could say with certainty that what the Gospel said about the crucifixion of the prophet of Galilee was true, and the centurion was right when he said, 'Truly he is the Son of God'. It was in the light of the Resurrection that I could read with certainty the story of the Gospel, knowing that everything was true in it because the impossible event of the Resurrection was to me more certain than any event of history. History I had to believe, the Resurrection I knew for a fact. I did not discover, as you see, the Gospel beginning with its first message of the Annunciation, and it did not unfold for me as a story which one can believe or disbelieve. It began as an event that left all problems of disbelief behind because it was a direct and personal experience.[27]

Thus the findings of modern scientific study, that apparent experiences of God are common and to be expected, are in full accord with Christian history.

Further analysis by the Alister Hardy Research Centre gives us an indication of the kinds of occasion on which religious experience occurs. Thus, we learn that nature is often important in these experiences: the subject is frequently alone in beautiful natural surroundings. More generally, an attitude of quiet and stillness is important. Then, in contrast, the presence of God is often experienced in times of acute physical or mental suffering. Yet again, the experiences often occur in response to prayer. In a sense of course God's presence is actively sought in prayer, in contrast to the occasions mentioned above when the experience is mainly involuntary.

It is also of vital interest that these experiences are often life-changing — frequently an individual will completely change the direction of his life; in particular he will behave more ethically than previously, and a change of job to something more serving of one's fellow men is often noted.

Clearly these findings are of interest, not just scientifically, but to the Christian churches as well. It turns out that, although there is a strong correlation between church-going and religious experience, the latter is by no means confined to the former. Indeed, we have seen in Chapter 1 that only about 10% of the population in Britain are regular church-goers and the numbers professing traditional Christian beliefs have been in decline for some years. The position with regard to religious experience is complex. Thus many people who have religious experiences are not attached to a church, and many church-goers report no religious experience; some people who have had experiences are openly hostile to the church. Some of the experiences are similar to those found in religions other than Christianity (such as the Eastern mystical religions we discussed in Chapter 8).

So the question arises, doesn't this line of argument actually prove too much, undermining the uniqueness of Christianity and of Christ, which it is my purpose in this chapter to defend? In particular, aren't the Eastern religions which I have criticized earlier just as valid as Christianity, since religious experience is undoubtedly also encountered in them?

Scripture teaches that God has revealed himself through the creation. We have seen how St Paul actually argued from creation. But time and again creation is asserted as showing God's glory. To take one example, in Psalm 104:24 we read 'O LORD, how manifold are thy works! in wisdom hast thou made all: the earth is full of thy riches'. It is perhaps natural to find God in nature, then.

The great Christian apologist C. S. Lewis, an authority on world literature, and thereby on pagan mythologies and religions, believed that God was revealing himself there too, if only partially, his full revelation being in Christ. Many of these pagan religions had dying and rising gods, which Lewis sees as hints or shadows of the one, true Incarnation and Resurrection of Christ. Lewis also cites the examples of Virgil, who wrote a poem in which a virgin gives birth and a new child is sent from heaven, and Plato, who postulated a perfectly righteous man treated as a monster of wickedness — bound, scourged and impaled[28] (my translation of the *Rebublic* actually has him crucified[29]). He expresses the hope that Virgil and Plato will fully understand the reality to which their writings pointed, in heaven.

Clearly the churches need to be alive to provide the interpretative framework for the experiences of God which many of our contemporaries have. In this we can have no better example than St Paul himself. In preaching to the Athenians (Acts 17) he built on what they already knew about God. St Paul noticed an altar with the inscription 'TO THE UNKNOWN GOD', and went on to say, 'Whom therefore ye ignorantly worship, him declare I unto you'. He went on to quote from two Greek poets. Epimenides of Crete, who in Greek legend is supposed to have advised the erection of 'anonymous altars', addressed the Supreme God in the words 'For in Thee we live and move and have our being'. Also the quotation 'For we are also his offspring' is from the *Phaenomena*, an astronomical poem by Aratus of Cilicia.[30] So St Paul did not deny the validity of this knowledge of God which thinking Greeks had deduced from their own experience and contemplation. Nevertheless he did of course go on to say that God had 'winked at' the times of ignorance and men were now commanded to repent in the light of the appointed day of judgment, when the world would be judged by Christ whom God had raised from the dead (Acts 17:30,31).

If the kinds of experience I have described are so common, it is natural to ask why we do not hear more about them. It is clear that people do not in general talk about their experiences. Hay suggests that this is because of the deadening effect of our prevailing scientific culture. According to accepted (scientific?) norms such experiences cannot occur. If scientific explanations are the only kind of valid explanations, then there is no room for the numinous and the mystical. Indeed if I experience such things it is possible there may be something wrong with me — am I mentally unstable? Thoughts such as these, however conscious or otherwise, inhibit people from sharing what are truly enriching experiences.

This view of Hay's is borne out by the increase in reporting of experiences in more intimate interviews already noted. It is also even more dramatically borne out by a survey of teenage attitudes to religion carried out by Martin and Pluck,[31] which revealed a virtual absence of any kind of religious belief (although, confusingly, a bizarre acceptance of superstition, ghosts, horoscopes, etc). The interesting point is that the teenagers in this survey were interviewed together in groups, whereas in the Hardy Centre's surveys interviews, which give very different results, are one-to-one and thereby much more likely to elicit genuine personal beliefs.

Hay[32] uses the findings of all this research to falsify (*pace* Popper) two modern 'scientific' rationalizations of religious experience. Of course in a culture so influenced by scientific reductionism the transcendent cannot have real existence — it must have been invented and must have 'survival value' to have lasted so long. Karl Marx said, 'Religion is the sigh of the oppressed creature, the heart of a heartless world, just as it is the spirit of a spiritless situation. It is the opium of the people'. Religion is something which the oppressed invent to comfort themselves: sufferings in the here and now do not matter because there is a reward to be had in the afterlife. Hay's evidence, on the contrary, is that religious experience is reported more by the higher echelons of society than the so-called oppressed masses. There is a steady increase of reported experience both with level of education and social class.

Freud, in contrast, diagnosed religion as a form of neurosis, albeit a universal one. The symptoms are psychotic hallucinations and are associated with repressed sexuality. Again the findings of the Hardy Centre contradict this. Psychological well-being has been ascertained in their surveys using standard measures. It transpires that those who have religious experiences are generally better balanced, and also behave more ethically, than those who do not.

It is interesting here to compare Freud's views with those of his equally eminent early collaborator, C. G. Jung. On the basis of the same data Jung took quite the opposite view of its interpretation. Jung thought that belief in God was innate to man. He found that all patients who came to him in middle life for psychological treatment (the young were specifically excluded) were lacking in something the living religions gave to their adherents. They were healed only when they came to a spiritual awareness.[33] On being asked in a television interview about his own belief in God, Jung replied from his own experience, 'I don't need to believe in God, I know'.[34]

Jung's account is echoed in the story told by Preb. Richard Bewes of a modern eminent psychiatrist who in a lecture described how the therapy he suggests for many of his patients is an exercise in Christian meditation last thing at night before going to sleep.[35] Let me quote Richard Bewes's account:

> 'You know the uncanny way in which you can so often will yourself to wake up early, simply by instructing yourself the night before?' he challenged. 'It's the same principle here. I tell my patients to chew over the selected phrase from the Bible as they drift off to sleep. First thing in the morning — there it is again. *It's been with them all night.* I wouldn't claim that they all turned into devout Christians. But one thing I've noticed in countless instances. If they kept up the pattern night after night, their whole disposition and outlook at the end of a month was radically, even magically, improved.

With Richard Bewes we would eschew the word 'magically' and, with him, would rather echo the words of James 1:21: 'Receive with meekness the engrafted word, which is able to save your souls'. The psychiatrist's patients become whole as the word of God seeps into their very beings and becomes part of them. Such outcomes are wholly consonant with the Christian view that men are made by God to enjoy a relationship with him: when that relationship is neglected we are diminished as human beings and when it is fostered we become more completely what we are meant to be.

Summarizing, we have seen that religious experience is a very common phenomenon today, despite the adverse rationalist scientific culture in which we live. It surely makes most sense to interpret this data, not that religion is some form of defence mechanism against oppression nor a neurosis from which most of us are suffering, but rather that there is an objective reality behind these experiences. Such a view is not contradicted by scientific inquiry.

CHAPTER 11

Conclusion

It is said that when science finally peers over the crest of the mountain, it will find that religion has been sitting there all along.[1]

In the preceding chapters we have covered a good deal of ground. We began by showing that there are many scientists today, particularly writers of popular books, who adopt a reductionist approach. They see science as offering a complete explanatory scheme. To them, all phenomena will ultimately be explained in terms of fundamental physics. Biology is explained in terms of the 'selfish gene' and genes are explicable in chemical and physical terms. And in fundamental physics the quest is on for a Theory of Everything which, by combining gravity and quantum theory, will embrace all physical phenomena.

We have looked at the scientific view of the world, following the story from the primordial fireball of the Big Bang to the emergence of conscious beings able to speculate on the wonder of it all.

We have seen that the scientific view is based on a rational way of examining the world, involving isolation of the phenomena under investigation and the repeatability of experiments. Crucially, science is reliant on there being an underlying order which is there to be discovered. Nevertheless it is not totally secure in its findings. Scientific theories represent the best approximation we have at any given time to the way the world works. They are often overthrown, and in our own century, particularly in physics, radically new theories have been postulated which alter our whole way of looking at the world. However, we can agree that scientists are making genuine progress in comprehending reality, as an ever widening range of phenomena comes within the sway of known laws.

It was natural for science to arise in Western Christendom because, in contrast to ancient Greek or Eastern cultures, the material world was seen here as the good creation of an omnipotent and perfectly good Being. The natural world and Scripture are both God given. Science is the interpreter of the one and theology of the other. No conflict arises if, following the mainstream tradition of a long line of Christian thinkers, including Augustine and later Calvin and the Reformers, one seeks spiritual and not scientific information from Scripture. Indeed this was the tradition followed by the great scientists of the sixteenth and seventeenth centuries, Kepler, Galileo and others.

The notion of conflict between science and Christian faith is in fact largely the invention of Thomas Huxley and his associates in the nineteenth century. Huxley and his friends were great propagandists. It is still widely but quite falsely believed that Galileo was imprisoned, and even tortured, by the church, that Calvin opposed Copernicus, that the church opposed improvements in sanitation and the use of chloroform in child-birth, and that Huxley himself secured the intellectual burial of the Christian faith in his famous encounter with Bishop Wilberforce.

We have seen that the reductionist programme is seriously flawed. While reducing wholes to their parts is a perfectly valid and necessary component of scientific method, the idea that each science in the hierarchy of sciences can be reduced to the one below it seems unrealizable in practice. Rather, we see that at higher levels of organization phenomena emerge which were unpredictable from the lower level laws. Ontological reductionism, the position that we are nothing but atoms and molecules organized in a particular way, is an unjustified metaphysical belief.

We have seen that in mathematics there is a fundamental barrier to what can be known by executing algorithmic procedures. There are things which can be known by humans which no machine can ever prove. Mathematics and therefore physics are incomplete.

We have seen emergent phenomena even within physics itself. We have also seen that the old idea of a clockwork universe is dead. The new physics allows a much greater freedom to nature than the older mechanistic theories. In particular there is an allowance for free agents, human beings, to exist where previously a blind determinism reigned.

The reductionist idea that the human mind does not really exist, or at best is an epiphenomenon of the brain, having no causal influence, has been seen to be erroneous. The idea that man is a computer is also demonstrably false. The idea that, in particular, he is a 'gene survival machine' fails to recognise not only Gödel's theorem but also the free will humans have to satisfy or deny their carnal instincts.

There have been a number of reactions against the shallowness of reductionism in science in recent years. They range from an outright rejection of science itself to attempts to read spiritual lessons from some of the more modern developments in science. The rejection of science is obscurantist and unnecessary. What is to be rejected is the reductionist philosophical outlook adopted by many scientists. On the other hand, the idea that Eastern mystics have somehow known all about quantum mechanics through their contemplations seems a little far fetched. When some of the supposed analogies are examined, they tend to fall apart. However, the Gaia theory we examined in Chapter 8 does seem to have genuine merit as a holistic scientific theory. As with quantum mysticism, though, the spiritual conclusion, in this case that the world or nature is in some sense God's body, seems to lack credibility. Care for the environment is in any case a natural interest of orthodox Christian believers who maintain that the universe is the good creation of a loving God who has made us stewards over that creation.

However, the newer theories of physics do genuinely seem to accord better with a religious outlook on life than did their predecessors. Modern cosmology, particularly the fine-tuning of the universe uncovered by cosmologists, points again to design and the existence of a designer. Moreover, there is room for God to act in the world which is governed by laws which are non-deterministic and with non-predictable outcomes.

In any case the Christian view of the world can stand on its own two feet as a rational account. Scientific study of its foundation documents has dispelled naïve views of their being given by 'divine dictation'. Nevertheless their intrinsic reliability in all essentials has been confirmed, particularly in the case of the New Testament, and there especially the gospels where Christ is revealed as Son of God. We have a faithful text of the New Testament; we know fairly well when and by whom most of it was composed; and we know of the earlier documents and eye-witness accounts which were used in its composition. That Christ was an historical figure who died on a cross under Pontius Pilate and whose remarkable character and doings were much as described in the gospels we can have little doubt.

The further strand of evidence we have for the Christian faith is religious experience. We find that this is remarkably common and that recorded experiences can be categorized into a few oft-repeated types. The best explanation for such experiences is that there is an objective reality behind them. This is certainly a simpler and, I believe, better explanation than Marxist or Freudian alternatives.

What I have attempted to do in this book is to demonstrate the falsehood of the reductionist position. I have endeavoured to show that there is more to life and the universe than the reductionists would have us believe. I have tried to show that theism, and in particular Christianity, is a much better intellectual option.

Let me end on a different note. While it is good to use our minds to examine matters of faith, it is more important still to put our everyday lives under God and his word. Only so shall we find answers to the questions of ultimate importance — how we find redemption and peace with God. Moreover, as we noted as long ago as Chapter 1, science does not of itself provide us with an ethical system, yet it raises many ethical issues. The Christian faith has insights here which are of vital importance to the way science is researched and applied in our modern world. This must be done with the humility stemming from a realization that what we are uncovering are the laws of nature given by God. We must have respect for our fellow men as the pinnacle of God's creation, made in his image and therefore of infinite worth, and, as noted earlier, we must also have due regard for the natural world as his creation which has been entrusted to us as stewards by him.

Finally, to those who have come thus far and who would wish to extend their exploration of the issues raised, I would recommend further reading from the many references I have given in this book. But supremely I would point to the Bible itself. It is there that, like the psychiatrist's patients, we shall find that which will make us whole and we shall be able to say with the psalmist (Psalm 119:105):

Thy word is a lamp unto my feet, and a light unto my path.

APPENDIX

Matters Mathematical

I'm very well acquainted too with matters mathematical,
I understand equations, both the simple and quadratical,
About binomial theorem I'm teeming with a lot o' news,
With many cheerful facts about the square of the hypotenuse.

(W. S. Gilbert, *Pirates of Penzance*.)

I have included this appendix for those readers who are not afraid of equations, though in any case I have endeavoured to keep things simple.

There are three topics covered here, the first two of which relate to items covered in Chapter 6 and the third to the matter of Chapter 9. The topics are: (a) Cantor's proof that there are more real numbers than fractions; (b) a simplified proof of Gödel's theorem; and (c) Bayes's theorem in probability theory.

Introduction to transfinite arithmetic

What would life be without arithmetic, but a scene of horrors?

(Rev Sydney Smith, *Letter to Miss* ——— , 22 July 1835.)

Before sketching Cantor's proof, let us define more precisely just what the various sets of numbers referred to in the main text of Chapter 6 are. First, the natural numbers are the non-negative whole numbers, 0, 1, 2, 3, and so on. 'Rationals' is the technical mathematical name for the fractions, and reals means all numbers including those like $\sqrt{2}$ and π which cannot be represented precisely as fractions.

The proof that there is a one-to-one correspondence between the natural numbers and the rationals amounts to the same thing as saying that we can write the latter in a list which includes all of them. Such a list could be

0, 1, 1/1, 2/1, 1/2, 3/1, 2/2, 1/3, 1/4, 2/3, 3/2, 4/1, ...

What we have done here is list the rationals whose numerator and denominator add up to 0, then to 1, then to 2, then to 3, and so on.

In fact this list multiply counts (2/2 is the same as 1/1) but that does not mean there are fewer rationals than natural numbers! The point is simply that any fraction you care to name would eventually crop up in this list. Hence the degree of infinity (called the 'cardinality') of the rationals, as for the natural numbers, is called 'countably infinite'.

Cantor demonstrated that one cannot do the same thing for the reals by supposing to start with that one can. This is the method of *reductio ad absurdum* so beloved of mathematicians. Start from what you are trying to disprove and show that it leads to a contradiction! Let us, then, assume that the following list of decimals includes all the reals between 0 and 1 in some order:

0.135329...
0.406839...
0.492394...
0.390120...

and so on.

What we do first is to construct a number whose first digit is identical to the first digit of the first number in the list, whose second digit is identical to the second digit of the second number in the list, whose third digit is identical to the third digit of the third number in the list, and so on. This new number consists of the digits highlighted in bold type in our original sequence:

0.1021...

If we then alter this number in each digit, for example by adding 1 to each digit, we can construct a new number

0.2132...

which is not in the list because it differs from each number in the list, eg from the nth number in the nth digit. Hence the list cannot include all the reals, so the reals have greater 'cardinality' than the rationals.

As stated in the text of Chapter 6, the continuum hypothesis, that there is no set with cardinality greater than that of the natural numbers but less than that of the reals, can be neither proved nor disproved from the axioms of set theory. This brings us to the quite startling work on the foundations of mathematics of the great Kurt Gödel.

Simplified proof of Gödel's theorem

We must never assume that which is incapable of proof.

(George Henry Lewes, *The Physiology of Common Life*, chapter 13.)

What Gödel did was to assign to each statement of number theory a code or 'Gödel number'. Thus, adapting Penrose's simplified notation,[1] statements about the single number w only were labelled $S_n(w)$, for n = 1, 2, 3, ... For example the 15th statement $S_{15}(w)$ might read

The sum of the first w natural numbers, call this $F(w)$, is given by the formula:

$$F(w) = \tfrac{1}{2}w(w+1)$$

Thus $S_{15}(3)$ is the statement that $1 + 2 + 3$ is the same as $\frac{1}{2}$ x 3 x 4, easily verified for a particular case. We are interested in establishing the truth or falsehood of all statements $S_n(w)$.

Now, very cleverly, Gödel also assigned a number to each sequence of logical steps or 'proofs' within his system. Let us call these proofs P_m, where m = 1, 2, 3, ... The proofs are connected chains of axioms and previously proved theorems joined by deductive rules. For example the proof of $S_{15}(w)$ might be P_{132}, and might comprise the following steps:

If $S_{15}(w)$ is true for $w = k$ then $F(k) = \frac{1}{2}k(k+1)$

which implies $F(k+1) = \frac{1}{2}k(k+1) + k+1$

ie $F(k+1) = \frac{1}{2}(k+1)(k+2)$

ie $S_{15}(w)$ is true for $w = k+1$

Moreover, $F(1) = 1$ and $\frac{1}{2}$ x 1 x 2 = 1 so $S_{15}(w)$ is true for $w = 1$.

Therefore $S_{15}(w)$ is true for all w.

The above is an example of proof by *mathematical induction*, a rigorous logical procedure, unlike induction in science which we discussed in Chapter 3. If the truth of the statement for a particular value of w implies its truth for the next value, *and* the statement is true for the first value of w, then it follows that it is true for all values of w.

Clearly all propositions and proofs would have to be very carefully and formally coded (this is done using symbols). Yet we can see in principle from this simple example how Gödel's scheme works.

Assuming, then, that we have at least in principle devised listings of all arithmetic statements and all proofs, let us now consider the wth statement about w, ie $S_w(w)$. We can formulate another arithmetic statement as follows:

There is no m such that $\mathbf{P}_m$ proves $\mathbf{S}_w(w)$.

Let us call this new statement $\mathbf{S}_k(w)$ so that:

There is no m such that $\mathbf{P}_m$ proves $\mathbf{S}_w(w) = \mathbf{S}_k(w)$

Now the trick is to apply $\mathbf{S}_k(w)$ to k itself. We obtain, by putting w equal to k:

There is no m such that $\mathbf{P}_m$ proves $\mathbf{S}_k(k) = \mathbf{S}_k(k)$.

We have now brought into the heart of arithmetic the English language paradoxical statement, 'This sentence is unprovable', as stated in Chapter 6. For if we examine $\mathbf{S}_k(k)$, we find that it asserts of itself that it cannot be proved. If there were such a proof then $\mathbf{S}_k(k)$ would be false by implication. If $\mathbf{S}_k(k)$ were false it would follow that there was a proof of $\mathbf{S}_k(k)$! That would violate the consistency of the scheme, since we cannot sensibly allow proofs of false statements. Hence $\mathbf{S}_k(k)$ must be true! What a fine mess you've got us into, Mr Gödel!

Bayes's Theorem

Lest men suspect your tale untrue
Keep probability in view.

(John Gay.)

In Chapter 9 we introduced Bayes's theorem as a means of evaluating evidence for an hypothesis, particularly that of the existence of God, mathematically. I now briefly summarize what the theorem says and how it can be so used.

If A and B are hypotheses, we use the notation P[A] to mean the *a priori* probability of A and P[A | B] to mean the probability of A given that we know B to be true. Then Bayes's theorem is a straightforward consequence of the axioms of probability theory. It states:

$$P[A \mid B] = \frac{P[B \mid A]P[A]}{P[B]}$$

Expanding the denominator we can also obtain the expression

$$P[A \mid B] = \frac{P[B \mid A]P[A]}{P[B \mid A]P[A] + P[B \mid \sim A]P[\sim A]}$$

where $\sim A$ means the negation of A.

Let us now consider the hypotheses G that there is a God and U that there is a complex physical universe. Then we have

$$P[G \mid U] = \frac{P[U \mid G]P[G]}{P[U \mid G]P[G] + P[U \mid \sim G]P[\sim G]}$$

Swinburne would further condition all these probabilities as also given background tautological information.

Suppose, then, that we believe sceptically that the prior probability of the existence of God is very low, say 1 in 1,000. On Swinburne's argument the probability that there is a universe given that there is no God $P[U \mid \sim G]$, should be much lower than this, say 1 in 1,000,000. The probability that there is a universe given God's existence will be larger than this, say 1 in 100. Substituting these numbers into the above we obtain

$$P[G \mid U] = 0.91.$$

The point is that this is very much bigger than the 1 in 1,000 *a priori* figure we started from, indeed not far short of certainty in this case. Hence the existence of a complex physical universe if good corroborative evidence for the existence of God.

In fact we shall always obtain corroboration, in the sense that $P[G \mid U] > P[G]$ provided that

$$P[U \mid G] > P[U \mid {\sim}G]$$

ie provided we are ready to agree that a complex physical universe is more likely given the existence of God than without him.

What Richard Dawkins seems to be saying is that $P[G] < P[U]$. While Swinburne, with some reason as explained in the text, would deny this (G is simple and U complex), it is not necessary to the argument to believe this about the *a priori* probabilities.

The great dispute about the use of Bayes's theorem in this way really centres on the inability to assign probabilities to put into the equation, and especially the prior probabilities. However, it does seem to be possible to make legitimate judgments about the conditional probabilities. The inequality $P[U \mid G] > P[U \mid {\sim}G]$ seems very plausible, though to confirm it would entail careful consideration of all 'no God' hypotheses. It is this inequality which leads one to conclude that the universe is good evidence, although perhaps not conclusive evidence, for God's existence. Also, if one approaches Bayes's theorem with subjective 'degrees of belief' to put into the equation then the theorem does show how these should be modified in the light of evidence.

I have inevitably avoided many subtleties in the arguments based on Bayes's theorem, and refer the reader to Swinburne and Bartholomew for differing points of view on the subject; and also to Carnap and Weatherford for the philosophical background to probability theory, and to Kingman and Taylor for a mathematical textbook.

NOTES

Chapter 1

1   Donald M. MacKay, *The Clockwork Image: A Christian Perspective on Science* (Inter-Varsity Press, London, 1974)

2. Jawaharlal Nehru (1889-1964), First Prime Minister of India, *Proceedings of the National Institute of Science of India* 27A (196): 564. Quoted in Max Perutz, *Is Science Necessary? Essays on Science and Scientists* (Oxford University Press, Oxford, 1991)

3. *Social Trends* 23, (HMSO, 1993), pp 153-154.

4. *Daily Telegraph*, December 24th, 1989.

5. Richard Dawkins, *The Blind Watchmaker* (Penguin, London, 1988), p 3.

6. Mary Midgley, *Science as Salvation: A modern myth and its meaning* (Routledge, London, 1992), p 9.

7. Richard Dawkins, *The Selfish Gene* (Oxford University Press, Oxford, 1989), p 2.

8. Richard Dawkins, *The Blind Watchmaker*, p 147.

9. Richard Dawkins, *Daily Telegraph Science Extra*, September 11th, 1989, p xi.

10. Richard Dawkins, Letter to *The Independent*, 22nd March, 1993.

11. Stephen Hawking, *A Brief History of Time* (Bantam, London, 1988), p 13.

12. *Ibid.*, p 122.

13. *Ibid.*, p 136.

14. D. A. Wilkinson, 'The Revival of Natural Theology in Contemporary Cosmology', *Science and Christian Belief*, Vol 2 No 2, October 1990, pp 95-115, quoting F. J. Tipler, *Times Higher Education Supplement* 832, 1988, p 23.

15. Stephen Hawking, *A Brief History of Time*, pp 140-141.

16. P. W. Atkins, *The Creation* (W. H. Freeman & Co., Oxford, 1981), pp vii-viii.

17. *Ibid.*, pp 35-37.

18. *Ibid.*, p 39.

19. *Ibid.*, p 115.

20. *Ibid.*, p 115.

21. Carl Sagan, *Cosmos* (MacDonald Futura, London, 1981), p 4.

22. Desmond Morris, *The Naked Ape* (Jonathan Cape, London), 1967.

23. Desmond Morris, *The Human Zoo* (Triad Grafton, London), 1979.

24. Desmond Morris, *Manwatching* (Jonathan Cape, London), 1977.

25. Desmond Morris, *The Human Zoo*, p 23.

26. George Carey, *I Believe in Man* (Hodder and Stoughton, London), 1977, p 21.

27. Desmond Morris, *The Human Zoo*, pp 31-33.

28. Desmond Morris, *Manwatching*, pp 148-152.

29. Rodney Cotterill, *No Ghost in the Machine: Modern Science and the Brain, the Mind and the Soul* (Heinemann, London), 1989.

30. Lewis Wolpert, *The Unnatural Nature of Science* (Faber and Faber, London, 1992), pp 151-171.

31. Richard Dawkins, *The Blind Watchmaker*, p 263.

32. Fay Weldon, *The Times*/Dillons debate, 'How Dangerous is Science?', *The Times*, 12th May, 1992.

33. Bryan Appleyard, *The Times*/Dillons debate, 'How Dangerous is Science?', *The Times*, 12th May, 1992.

Chapter 2

1. D. W. Sciama, 'The origin of the Universe', in *The State of the Universe: Wolfson College Lectures 1979*, ed. G. Bath (Oxford University Press, Oxford, 1980).

2. R. J. Tayler, 'The origin of the elements', in *The State of the Universe: Wolfson College Lectures 1979*.

3. Charles Darwin, *The Origin of Species* 1859, in *The Illustrated Origin of Species*, abridged and introduced by Richard E. Leakey (Faber and Faber, London, 1979), p 75.

4. Adrian Desmond and James Moore, *Darwin* (Penguin, London, 1992), pp 209, 220.

5. John Maynard Smith, *The Theory of Evolution*, 3rd Edition (Penguin 1975), pp 185-191.

6. Richard Dawkins, *The Blind Watchmaker* (Penguin, London, 1988), chapters 2 and 4.

7. James D. Watson, *The Double Helix: A Personal Account of the Discovery of the Structure of DNA*, A New Critical Edition, Ed. Gunther S. Stent (Weidenfeld and Nicholson, London, 1981), p 115.

8. Albert Einstein, 'Science and Religion', *Nature* **146**, 1940, p 605.

9. Stanley Jaki, *The Road of Science and the Ways to God* (The University of Chicago Press, Chicago, 1978), p 294.

10. *Ibid.*, p 294.

11. Stephen Hawking, *A Brief History of Time*, (Bantam, London, 1988), p 174.

Chapter 3

1. Alexander Pope, *Epitaphs, Intended for Sir Isaac Newton*.

2. Frank E. Close, *Too Hot to Handle: The Story of the Race for Cold Fusion* (W H Allen, London, 1990).

3. John R. Huizenga, *Cold Fusion: The Scientific Fiasco of the Century* (University of Rochester Press, Rochester, N.Y., 1992).

4. Roger Penrose, *The Emperor's New Mind: Concerning Computers, Minds and the Laws of Physics* (Oxford University Press, Oxford, 1989), p 152ff.

5. Sir Karl Popper, *The Logic of Scientific Discovery* (Unwin Hyman Ltd, London, 1990), p 278.

230 *Nothing But Atoms And Molecules?*

6. *Ibid.*, p 280.

7. *Ibid.*, p 280.

8. John Polkinghorne, *One World: The interaction of science and theology*, (SPCK, London, 1986), p 22.

9. *Ibid.*, pp 22-23.

10. Albert Einstein, 'The Religiousness of Science' in *The World as I see It*, transl. Alan Harris, (John Lane, London, 1935), p 28.

11. Stanley L. Jaki, *Science and Creation: From eternal cycles to an oscillating universe* (Scottish Academic Press, Edinburgh, 1974).

12. R. Hooykaas, *Religion and the Rise of Modern Science* (Scottish Academic Press, Edinburgh, 1972).

13. John D. Barrow, *The World within the World* (Oxford University Press, Oxford, 1988), pp 31-35.

14. P A M Dirac, 'The evolution of the physicist's picture of nature', *Scientific American*, May 1963 (quoted in Paul Davies, *God and the New Physics* (Penguin, London, 1984), pp 220-221).

15. Banesh Hoffman, *Albert Einstein: Creator and Rebel*, quoted in A. P. French, editor, *Einstein: A Centenary Volume* (Heinemann, London, 1979), p 175.

16. Michael Polanyi, *Personal Knowledge: Towards a post-critical philosophy* (Routledge and Kegan Paul, London, 1958), pp 9-15.

17. Abraham Pais, *'Subtle is the Lord ...': The Science and the Life of Albert Einstein* (Oxford University Press, Oxford, 1982), p 113.

18. Thomas S. Kuhn, *The Structure of Scientific Revolutions* (University of Chicago Press, Chicago, 1980).

19. John Polkinghorne, *One World*, pp 13-14.

20. Karl Popper, quoted in John Barrow, *The World within the World*, p 179.

21. Abraham Pais, *'Subtle is the Lord ...'*, pp 111-119, 172.

22. D. W. Sciama, 'The origin of the Universe', in *The State of the Universe: Wolfson College Lectures 1979*, ed. G. Bath (Oxford University Press, Oxford, 1980).

23. *Ibid.*

24. Michael Green, *Evangelism through the Local Church* (Hodder and Stoughton, London, 1990), p 149.

25. A. R. Peacocke, *God and the New Biology: Were Matter, Life and Humanity Created?* (J M Dent & Sons Ltd, London, 1986), p 35.

26. Richard Dawkins, *The Blind Watchmaker* (Penguin, London), 1988, p 287.

27. Richard E. Leakey in Introduction to the *Illustrated Origin of Species* (Faber and Faber, London, 1979), p 15.

28. Richard Dawkins, *The Blind Watchmaker*, p 225.

29. I. G. Barbour, *Religion in an Age of Science* (SCM Press, London, 1990), p 157.

30. A. R. Peacocke, *God and the New Biology*, p 34.

31. John Maynard Smith, *The Theory of Evolution*, 3rd Edition (Penguin, Harmondsworth, 1975).

32. Richard Leakey in Introduction to the *Illustrated Origin of Species*, pp 18-19.

33. Sir James Jeans, *The Universe Around Us* (MacMillan, New York, 1929).

34. Quoted in Corey S. Powell, 'The Golden Age of Cosmology', *Scientific American*, July 1992.

Chapter 4

1. Charles Darwin, *Origin of Species* 1859, in *The Illustrated Origin of Species*, abridged and introduced by Richard E. Leakey (Faber and Faber, London, 1979), p 216.

2. Lewis Wolpert, *The Unnatural Nature of Science* (Faber and Faber, London, 1992), p 144.

3. Bertrand Russell, *The Impact of Science on Society* (Simon and Schuster, New York, 1953), p 7.

4. R. Hooykaas, *Religion and the Rise of Modern Science* (Scottish Academic Press, Edinburgh, 1972), p 39.

5. *Ibid.*, p 105.

6. *Ibid.*, p 49.

7. Arthur Koestler, *The Sleepwalkers* (Penguin, London, 1964).

8. Allan Chapman, 'A Year of Gravity: The Astronomical Anniversaries of 1992', *Quarterly Journal of the Royal Astronomical Society* (1993), 34, pp 33-51.

9. Arthur Koestler, *The Sleepwalkers*, p 195.

10. A. P. French, editor, *Einstein: A Centenary Volume* (Heinemann, London, 1979), p 41.

11. Arthur Koestler, *The Sleepwalkers*, p 470.

12. *Ibid.*, p 470.

13. *Ibid.*, p 480.

14. *Ibid.*, p 493.

15. *Ibid.*, p 498.

16. *Ibid.*, p 498.

17. *Ibid.*, p 498.

18. *Ibid.*, p 500.

19. *Ibid.*, p 503.

20. Gwyn MacFarlane, *Howard Florey: The Making of a Great Scientist* (Oxford University Press, Oxford, 1979), pp 19-24.

21. Adrian Desmond & James Moore, *Darwin* (Penguin, London, 1991), p 497.

22. *Ibid.*, p 492.

23. *Ibid.*, p 494.

24. John William Draper, *History of the Conflict between Religion and Science*, (The Pioneer Press, London, New Edition, 1923[issued by The Secular Society Limited]).

25. Owen Chadwick, *The Secularization of the European Mind in the Nineteenth Century* (Cambridge University Press, Cambridge, 1975), pp 161-163.

26. Colin A. Russell, 'The Conflict Metaphor and its Social Origins', *Science and Christian Belief*, Vol 1 No 1, April 1989, pp 5-8, 22.

27. Adrian Desmond and James Moore, *Darwin*, p 497.

28. *Ibid.*, p 497.

29. Clifford Longley, *The Times*, 9th May, 1992.

30. Colin A. Russell, *Cross-currents: Interactions between science and faith* (Inter-Varsity Press, Leicester, 1985), pp 167-168.

31. *Ibid.*, p 168.

32. Andrew D. White, *A History of the Warfare of Science with Theology in Christendom* (Arco Publishers Ltd, London, 1955 [first published 1895]), Vol II, p 55ff.

33. *Ibid.*, Vol I, p 142.

34. John William Draper, *History of the Conflict between Religion and Science*, pp 172-173.

35. Adrian Desmond and James Moore, *Darwin*, p 526.

36. Colin A. Russell, 'The Conflict Metaphor and its Social Origins', p 17.

37. *Ibid.*, p 19.

38. Adrian Desmond and James Moore, *Darwin*, p 527.

39. *Ibid.*, p 561.

40. *Ibid.*, p 560.

41. *Ibid.*, p 611 (part quotation).

42. Colin A. Russell, 'The Conflict Metaphor and its Social Origins', p 16 (full quotation).

43. Colin A. Russell, *Cross-currents: Interactions between science and faith*, p 190.

44. *Ibid.*, p 212.

45. *Ibid.*, p 212.

46. Colin A. Russell, 'The Conflict Metaphor and its Social Origins', p 26.

47. J. B. Lightfoot, *The Epistles of St. Paul II, The Third Apostolic Journey, 3, Epistle to the Galatians*, Preface to 1st edition, 8th edition (MacMillan, London, 1884).

48. Richard Dawkins, *The Independent*, 20th April, 1992; edited version of speech at the Edinburgh International Science Festival, 15th April, 1992.

49. Arthur Koestler, *The Sleepwalkers*, p 441.

50. *Ibid.*, p 441.

51. Colin A. Russell, *Cross-currents, Interactions between science and faith*, p 47.

52. *Ibid.*, p 47.

53. *Ibid.*, p 48.

54. R. Hooykaas, *Religion and the Rise of Modern Science*, p 121.

55. *Ibid.*, p 118.

56. *Ibid.*, pp 118-120.

57. St. Jerome, quoted in C. S. Lewis, *Miracles* (Collins, Fount Paperbacks edition, Glasgow, 1977), p 37.

58. St. Augustine of Hippo, *Confessions*, Book VI (Penguin Classics edition, Harmondsworth, 1961), section 4, p 115.

Chapter 5

1. John Barrow, *The World within the World* (Oxford University Press, Oxford, 1988), p 338.

2. F. J. Ayala, 'Introduction' in *Studies in the Philosophy of Biology: Reduction and Related Problems*, Ed. F. J. Ayala and T. Dobzhansky (MacMillan, London, 1974).

3. A. R. Peacocke, *God and the New Biology: Were Matter, Life and Humanity Created?* (J. M. Dent and Sons Ltd, London, 1986).

4. Ian G. Barbour, *Religion in an Age of Science* (SCM Press, London, 1990).

5. A. R. Peacocke, *God and the New Biology*, p 11.

6. *Ibid*, p 7.

7. David Bohm, *Wholeness and the Implicate Order* (Routledge, London, 1980), p 134.

8. *Ibid*, p 134.

9. F. H. C. Crick, *Of Molecules and Man* (University of Washington Press, Seattle, 1966), p 10, quoted in A. R. Peacocke, *God and the New Biology*, p 1.

10. Karl Popper, 'Scientific Reduction and the Essential Incompleteness of All Science', in *Studies in the Philosophy of Biology: Reduction and Related Problems*, p 260.

11. *Ibid*, pp 266-269.

12. Ernest Nagel, *The Structure of Science: Problems in the Logic of Scientific Explanation*, (Routledge and Kegan Paul, London, 1961), pp 353-354.

13. S. A. Barnett, *Biology and freedom* (Cambridge University Press, Cambridge, 1988), p 230.

14. F. J. Ayala, 'Introduction' in *Studies in the Philosophy of Biology: Reduction and Related Problems*, p xi.

15. Donald T. Campbell, "Downward Causation" in Hierarchically Organized Biological Systems in *Studies in the Philosophy of Biology: Reduction and Related Problems*, p 180.

16. Michael Polanyi, *Personal Knowledge: Towards a post-critical philosophy* (Routledge and Kegan Paul, London, 1958), pp 328-331.

17. A. R. Peacocke, *God and the New Biology*, p 25.

18. Donald T. Campbell, "Downward Causation" in Hierarchically Organized Biological Systems in *Studies in the Philosophy of Biology: Reduction and Related Problems*, p 181.

19. S. A. Barnett, *Biology and freedom*, pp 236-237.

20. F. J. Ayala, 'Introduction' in *Studies in the Philosophy of Biology: Reduction and Related Problems*, p viii.

21. Donald MacKay, *The Clockwork Image: A Christian Perspective on Science* (Inter-Varsity Press, London, 1974), pp 36-38, pp 43-44.

22. J. B. S. Haldane, *Possible Worlds*, p 209, quoted in C. S. Lewis, *Miracles* (Collins, Fount Paperbacks edition, Glasgow, 1977), p 19.

23. C. S. Lewis, *Miracles*.

24. Richard Dawkins, *The Selfish Gene* (Oxford University Press, Oxford, 1989), p v.

25. Richard Dawkins, *The Blind Watchmaker* (Penguin, London, 1988), p 10.

26. *Ibid*, p 15.

27. *Ibid*, p 126.

28. J. S. Jones, *The Language of the Genes* (HarperCollins, London, 1993), p xi.

29. Stephen Hawking, *A Brief History of Time* (Bantam, London, 1988), p 175.

Chapter 6

1. Roger Bacon, *Opus Majus Part 4 Distinctia Prima* cap 1, 1267 transl. Robert Belle Burke 1928 (University of Pennsylvania Press, Philadelphia PA).

2. Richard Dawkins, *The Selfish Gene* (Oxford University Press 1989), p 69ff.

3. Roger Penrose, *The Emperor's New Mind: Concerning Computers, Minds and the Laws of Physics* (Oxford University Press, Oxford, 1989), p 105ff.

4. Douglas Hofstadter, *Gödel, Escher and Bach* (Penguin, Harmondsworth, 1980), p 19.

5. Roger Penrose, *The Emperor's New Mind*, p 101.

6. John D. Barrow, *Pi in the Sky* (Oxford University Press, Oxford, 1992), p 264.

7. John D. Barrow, *The World within the World* (Oxford University Press, Oxford, 1988), p 258.

8. Roger Penrose, *The Emperor's New Mind*, p 146-147.

9. Russell Stannard, *The Times*, 13th Nov, 1989.

10. *Ibid.*

11. John D. Barrow, *Theories of Everything: The Quest for Ultimate Explanation* (Oxford University Press, Oxford, 1990), pp 37-38.

12. *Ibid.*, p 210.

13. *Ibid.*, p 210.

14. Paul Davies, *The Mind of God* (Simon and Schuster, London, 1992), p 167.

15. quoted in John D. Barrow, *The World within the World* (Oxford University Press, Oxford, 1988), p 275.

16. quoted in John D. Barrow, *The World within the World*, p 275.

17. Ian Stewart, *Does God Play Dice? The New Mathematics of Chaos* (Penguin, London, 1990,) p 70.

18. John Polkinghorne, *Science and Providence: God's Interaction with the World* (SPCK, London, 1989), p 28-29.

19. Paul Davies, *God and the New Physics*,(Penguin, London, 1984), p 137.

20. John Polkinghorne, *Reason and Reality: The Relationship between Science and Theology* (SPCK, London, 1991), p 41.

21. James Gleick, *Chaos: making a new science* (Cardinal, McDonald & Co, London, 1988), pp 121-153.

22. Ilya Prigogine and Isabelle Stengers, *Order out of Chaos: Man's New Dialogue with Nature* (Collins, Fontana Paperbacks edition, London, 1985), p 13.

23. *Ibid.*, p 291ff.

24. John Polkinghorne, *Reason and Reality*, p 38.

25. D. W. Sciama, *The physical foundations of general relativity* (Heinemann, London, 1972), pp 18-19.

26. John Polkinghorne, *Science and Providence: God's Interaction with the World*, p 29.

Chapter 7

1. Gilbert Ryle, *The Concept of Mind* (Penguin Edition, London, 1990), p 17.

2. Sir Karl Popper in Karl R. Popper and John C. Eccles, *The Self and Its Brain* (Springer International, Berlin, 1977), p 105.

3. B. F. Skinner, *Beyond Freedom and Dignity* (Alfred A. Knopf, New York, 1971).

4. Sir John Eccles in F. J. Ayala and T. Dobzhansky (eds.), *Studies in the Philosophy of Biology* (MacMillan, London, 1974), p 89.

5. Sir Karl Popper in Karl Popper and John Eccles, *The Self and Its Brain*, p 74.

6. Herbert Feigl, *The 'Mental' and the 'Physical'* (University of Minnesota Press, Minneapolis, Minnesota, 1967).

7. Sir John Eccles in Ayala and Dobzhansky, p 90.

8. Roger Penrose, *The Emperor's New Mind: Concerning Computers, Minds and the Laws of Physics* (Oxford University Press, Oxford, 1989).

9. Sir John Eccles in Karl Popper & John Eccles, *The Self and its Brain*, p 318.

10. Sir John Eccles, *Evolution of the Brain: Creation of the Self* (Routledge, London and New York, 1989), p 210.

11. Sir Karl Popper in Karl Popper & John Eccles, *The Self and Its Brain*, p 144.

12. Donald M. MacKay, *The Open Mind and other essays*, ed. Melvin Tinker (Inter-Varsity Press, London, 1988), p 47.

13. S. A. Barnett, *Biology and freedom* (Cambridge University Press, Cambridge, 1988), p 233.

14. Sir John Eccles in Ayala and Dobzhansky, p 99.

15. Sir Karl Popper, *Objective Knowledge: An Evolutionary Approach*, Revised Edition (Oxford Univerity Press, Oxford, 1979), pp 223-224.

16. Sir John Eccles in Ayala and Dobzhansky, p 102.

17. John Searle, *Minds, Brains and Science: The 1984 Reith Lectures* (Penguin, London, 1984), pp 80-82.

18. Donald MacKay, 'In What Sense Can a Computer "Understand"?', *Science and Christian Belief*, Vol 1 No 1, April 1989, pp 27-39.

19. Donald M. MacKay, *The Open Mind and other essays*, p 55.

20. *Ibid.*, p 56.

21. Donald M. MacKay, *Behind the Eye*, ed. Valerie MacKay (Blackwell, Oxford, 1991), p 9.

22. David G Myers and Malcolm A Jeeves, *Psychology through the eyes of faith* (Inter-Varsity Press, London, 1991), pp 20-22.

23. Donald M. MacKay, *Behind the Eye*, pp 194-204.

24. Donald M. MacKay, *Brains, Machines and Persons* (Collins, London, 1980), p 94.

25. Richard Dawkins, *The Blind Watchmaker* (Penguin, London, 1988), p 195.

26. W D Hamilton, 'The genetical evolution of social behaviour' (I and II), *Journal of Theoretical Biology*, 7, 1964, pp 1-16; 17-52.

27. J B S Haldane, *New Scientist*, 8 August, 1974, p 325.

28. Richard Dawkins, *The Selfish Gene* (Oxford University Press, Oxford, 1989), p 100.

29. Christopher Bryant, *Depth Psychology and Religious Belief* (Darton, Longman and Todd, London, 1987).

30. H W Robinson, *The Christian Doctrine of Man*, 3rd edition (T&T Clark, Edinburgh, 1926), p 27.

31. G Carey, *I believe in Man* (Hodder and Stoughton, London, 1977), pp 27-29.

32. Richard Dawkins, *The Blind Watchmaker*, p 93.

33. *Ibid*, p 1.

34. *Ibid*, p 188.

35. Roger Penrose, *The Emperor's New Mind; Concerning Computers, Minds and the Laws of Physics* (Oxford University Press, Oxford, 1989), p 8.

36. John Searle, *Minds, Brains and Science: The 1984 Reith Lectures*.

37. J. R. Lucas, 'Minds, Machines and Gödel', *Philosophy* **36**, 1961, pp 120-124, reprinted in Alan Ross Anderson, *Minds and Machines* (Prentice-Hall Inc., Englewood Cliffs, 1964), pp 43-59.

Chapter 8

1. Jacques Monod, *Chance and Necessity: An essay on the natural philosophy of modern biology*, transl. Austryn Wainhouse (Collins, London, 1972), p 161.

2. Bryan Appleyard, *Understanding the Present* (Pan Books, London, 1992).

3. *Ibid*, p 2.

4. *Ibid*, p 16.

5. *Ibid*, p 95.

6. *Ibid*, p 200.

7. *Ibid*, p 108.

8. *Ibid*, p 108.

9. *Ibid*, p 85.

10. *Ibid.*, p 229.

11. Martin Buber, *I and Thou*, Eng. trans. by Ronald Gregor Smith (T&T Clark, Edinburgh, 1937).

12. *Ibid.*, p 11.

13. Mary Midgley, *Science as Salvation: A modern myth and its meaning* (Routledge, London, 1992).

14. P. W. Atkins, *The Creation* (W. H. Freeman & Co., Oxford, 1981), p 127.

15. John D. Barrow and Frank J. Tipler, *The Anthropic Cosmological Principle* (Oxford University Press, Oxford, 1986), pp 658-677.

16. Fritjof Capra, *The Tao of Physics: An Exploration of the Parallels between Modern Physics and Eastern Mysticism* (Shambhala, Berkeley, 1975).

17. *Ibid*, p 270.

18. J. C. Polkinghorne, *The Quantum World* (Longman, Harlow, 1984), p 66.

19. Fritjof Capra, *The Tao of Physics*, p 285.

20. John D. Barrow, *The World Within The World* (Oxford University Press, Oxford, 1988), pp 174-177.

21. Fritjof Capra, *The Tao of Physics*, p 257.

22. *Ibid.*, p 257.

23. John. D. Barrow, *The World Within The World*, p 180.

24. J. E. Lovelock, *Gaia: A new look at life on Earth* (Oxford University Press, Oxford, 1979), p 10.

25. *Ibid*, p 52.

26. *Ibid*, p 69.

27. *Ibid.*, pp 70-72.

28. Richard Dawkins, *The Extended Phenotype* (Oxford University Press, Oxford, 1982), pp 234-237.

29. James Lovelock, *The Ages of Gaia: A biography of our living Earth* (Oxford University Press), Oxford, 1988, pp 36-39.

30. Hugh Montefiore, *The Probability of God* (SCM Press, London, 1985), pp 43-58.

31. James Lovelock, *The Ages of Gaia*, p 205.

32. *Ibid.*, p 206.

33. Grace M. Jantzen, *God's World, God's Body* (Darton, Longman and Todd, London, 1984).

34. Sallie McFague, *Models of God* (SCM Press, London), 1987.

35. C. S. Lewis, *Reflections on the Psalms* (Collins, Fount Paperbacks Edition, Glasgow, 1977), p 69.

36. Lawrence Osborn, 'The Machine and the Mother Goddess: The Gaia Hypothesis in Contemporary Scientific and Religious Thought', *Science and Christian Belief*, Vol 4 No 1, April 1992, pp 27-41.

37. R. J. Berry, 'Christianity and the Environment: Escapist Mysticism or Responsible Stewardship', *Science and Christian Belief*, Vol 3 No 1, April 1991, pp 3-18.

38. Ron Elsdon, *Greenhouse Theology: Biblical Perspectives on Caring for Creation* (Monarch, Speldhurst, Kent, 1992).

Chapter 9

1. Richard Dawkins, *The Blind Watchmaker* (Penguin, London, 1988), p 147.

2. Immanuel Kant, *Critique of Pure Reason*, transl J. M. D. Meiklejohn, Everyman edition (J. M. Dent and Sons, London), 1991, p 349.

3. Richard Swinburne, *The Existence of God*, Revised Edition (Oxford University Press, Oxford, 1991).

4. Rudolf Carnap, *Logical Foundations of Probability* (Routledge and Kegan Paul, London), 1950.

5. Roy Weatherford, *Philosophical Foundations of Probability Theory* (Routledge and Kegan Paul, London, 1982).

6. J. F. C. Kingman and S. J. Taylor, *Introduction to Measure and Probability* (Cambridge University Press, Cambridge, 1966).

7. Anthony Garrett, 'Ockham's razor', *Physics World*, May 1991, p 39.

8.   Richard Dawkins, *The Blind Watchmaker*, p 316.

9.   Richard Swinburne, *The Existence of God*, p 94.

10. John D. Barrow and Frank J. Tipler, *The Anthropic Cosmological Principle* (Oxford University Press, Oxford, 1986).

11. Paul Davies, *The Accidental Universe* (Cambridge University Press, Cambridge, 1982).

12. John Polkinghorne, *The Way the World is* (SPCK, London, 1983).

13. John Polkinghorne, *One World: The interaction of science and theology* (SPCK, London, 1986).

14. John Polkinghorne, *Science and Creation: The search for understanding* (SPCK, London, 1988).

15. John Polkinghorne, *Science and Providence: God's interaction with the world* (SPCK, London, 1989).

16. John Polkinghorne, *Reason and Reality* (SPCK, London, 1991).

17. Richard Swinburne, *The Existence of God*, Appendix.

18. Ian Barbour, *Religion in an Age of Science* (SCM Press, London, 1990).

19. Hugh Montefiore, *The Probability of God* (SCM Press, London, 1985).

20. John D. Barrow and Frank J. Tipler, *The Anthropic Cosmological Principle*, p 385.

21. *Ibid.*, p 399.

22. Paul Davies, *The Accidental Universe*, p 63.

23. John D. Barrow and Frank J.Tipler, *The Anthropic Cosmological Principle*, pp 252-253.

24. Paul Davies, *The Accidental Universe*, pp 117-118.

25. Paul Davies, *God and the New Physics* (Penguin, London, 1984), p 168.

26. Roger Penrose, *The Emperor's New Mind: Concerning Computers, Minds and the Laws of Physics* (Oxford University Press, Oxford, 1989), pp 339-345.

27. *Ibid.*, p 344.

28. John Polkinghorne, *Science and Creation: The Search for Understanding*, p 23.

29. *Ibid.*, p 23.

30. D. W. Sciama in *The Anthropic Principle: Proceedings of the Second Venice Conference on Cosmology and Philosophy*, ed. F. Bertola and U. Curi (Cambridge University Press, Cambridge, 1989), pp 109-111.

31. Paul Davies, *The Mind of God* (Simon and Schuster, London, 1992), pp 204-205.

32. John Polkinghorne, 'The Mind of God?', *The Cambridge Review*, March 1992.

33. Donald M MacKay, *The Open Mind and other essays*, ed. Melvin Tinker (Inter-Varsity Press, London, 1988), p 214; reprinted from *Faith and Thought*, Vol 113, No 2, 1987.

34. Donald M MacKay, *Science, Chance and Providence*, Riddell Memorial Lectures, University of Newcastle upon Tyne 1977 (Oxford University Press, Oxford, 1978), pp 4-9.

35. Maurice Wiles, *God's Action in the World: The Bampton Lectures for 1986* (SCM Press, London, 1986), p 28.

36. William G. Pollard, *Chance and Providence: God's Action in a World Governed by Scientific Law* (Faber and Faber, London, 1958); Pollard's position is reviewed in David J. Bartholomew, *God of Chance* (SCM Press, London, 1984), pp 125-134.

37. Donald M MacKay, *Science, Chance and Providence*, pp 30-31.

38. David J. Bartholomew, *God of Chance* (SCM Press, London, 1984), pp 129-130.

39. A. N. Whitehead, *Process and Reality* (Cambridge University Press, Cambridge, 1929).

40. John B. Cobb, Jr., and David Ray Griffin, *Process Theology: An Introductory Exposition* (Christian Journals Limited, Belfast, 1977), p 51.

41. *Ibid.*, p 53.

42. J. R. Lucas, *Freedom and Grace: Essays* (SPCK, London, 1976), p 39.

43. John Houghton, *Does God Play Dice?* (Inter-Varsity Press, Leicester, 1988), p 124.

44. David J. Bartholomew, *God of Chance*, p 139.

45. Ibid., pp 140-141.

46. Donald M MacKay, *Science, Chance and Providence*.

47. John Houghton, 'A God Big Enough' in *Real Science, Real Faith*, ed. R. J. Berry (Monarch Publications, Eastbourne, 1991), p 43.

48. C. S. Lewis, *Miracles* (Collins, Fount Paperbacks edition, Glasgow, 1977), pp 105-106.

49. R. J. Berry, 'What to believe about miracles', *Nature* **322**, 1986, pp 321-322.

50. C. S. Lewis, *Miracles*, p 112.

51. Keith Ward, *Divine Action* (Collins, London, 1990).

Chapter 10

1. St. Anselm, *Cur Deus Homo?* (John Grant, Edinburgh, 1909), I.XX, pp 47-49.

2. *Ibid.*, II.VI, p 67.

3. *Ibid.*, II.VII, p 68; NB Anselm's argument is discussed in John R. W. Stott, *The Cross of Christ* (Inter-Varsity Press, Leicester, 1986), p 119.

4. Richard Dawkins, *The Selfish Gene* (Oxford University Press, Oxford, 1989), p 198.

5. *Ibid.*, p 330, note.

6. John A. T. Robinson, *Can We Trust the New Testament?* (A. R. Mowbray, Oxford, 1977), p 35.

7. Stephen Neill & Tom Wright, *The Interpretation of the New Testament 1861-1986*, Second Edition (Oxford University Press, Oxford, 1988).

8. F. F. Bruce, *The New Testament Documents: Are they Reliable?* 5th Edition (Inter-Varsity Fellowship, London, 1960), p 39.

9. *Ibid.*, p 33.

10. John A. T. Robinson, *The Priority of John*, ed. J. F. Coakley (SCM Press, London, 1985).

11. John A. T. Robinson, *Redating the New Testament* (SCM Press, London, 1976).

12. C. S. Lewis, *Miracles*, (Collins, Fount Paperbacks edition, Glasgow, 1977), p 99.

13. Stephen Neill & Tom Wright, *The Interpretation of the New Testament 1861-1986*, p 153.

14. C. J. Humphreys & W. G. Waddington, 'Dating the Crucifixion', *Nature*, **306**, pp 743-746, 1983.

15. J. P. Pratt, 'Newton's Date for the Crucifixion', *Quarterly Journal of the Royal Astronomical Society*, **32**, pp 301-304, 1991.

16. D. H. Clark, J. H. Parkinson, & F. R. Stephenson, 'An Astronomical Re-Appraisal of the Star of Bethlehem — A Nova in 5 BC', *Quarterly Journal of the Royal Astronomical Society*, **18**, pp 443-449, 1977.

17. C. J. Humphreys, 'The Star of Bethlehem—a Comet in 5 BC— and the Date of the Birth of Christ', *Quarterly Journal of the Royal Astronomical Society*, **32**, pp 349-407, 1991.

18. Ivor Bulmer-Thomas, 'The Star of Bethlehem — A New Explanation — Stationary Point of a Planet', *Quarterly Journal of the Royal Astronomical Society*, **33**, pp 363-374, 1992.

19. Lesslie Newbigin, *Foolishness to the Greeks: The Gospel and Western Culture* (SPCK, London, 1986), p 17.

20. William James, *The Varieties of Religious Experience: The Gifford Lectures 1901-1902* (Collins, Fount Paperbacks, Glasgow, 1977).

21. David Hay, *Religious Experience Today*, (Mowbray, London, 1990).

22. Alister Hardy, *The Spiritual Nature of Man: A study of contemporary religious experience* (Oxford University Press, Oxford, 1979).

23. Rudolph Otto, *Das Heilige*, Eng. trans. by J. W. Harvey, *The Idea of the Holy* (Oxford University Press, Oxford, 2nd edition, 1950, paperback edition, 1958).

24. David Hay, *Exploring Inner Space* (Mowbray, London, 1987), p 152.

25. David Hay, *Religious Experience Today*, pp 43-44.

26. *Ibid.*, p 44.

27. Anthony Bloom, *School for Prayer* (Darton, Longman and Todd, London, 1970), p xii.

28. C. S. Lewis, *Reflections on the Psalms* (Collins, Fount Paperbacks edition, Glasgow, 1977), chapter X.

29. Plato, *Republic* (J. M. Dent and Sons, London, 1935), II.362, p 39.

30. F. F. Bruce, 'The Acts of the Apostles', in *The New Bible Commentary Revised*, ed. D. Guthrie, J. A. Motyer, A. M. Stibbs, D. J. Wiseman (Inter-Varsity Press, London, 1970).

31. Bernice Martin and Ronald Pluck, *Young People's Beliefs*, Church of England Board of Education 1977, quoted in David Hay, *Religious Experience Today*, pp 97-98.

32. David Hay, *Religious Experience Today*, pp 86-90.

33. Christopher Bryant, *Depth Psychology and Religious Belief* (Darton, Longman and Todd, London, 1987), p 5.

34. Quoted in Christopher Bryant, *Depth Psychology and Religious Belief*, p 32.

35. Richard Bewes, *Talking about Prayer* (Falcon Books, Eastbourne, 1979), p 73.

Chapter 11

1. Quoted by Peter O'Toole in Universal Pictures' *Creator*.

Appendix

1. Roger Penrose, *The Emperor's New Mind: Concerning Computers, Minds and the Laws of Physics* (Oxford University Press, Oxford, 1989), pp 102-108.

INDEX